AUTO ANTENNA

An Enchanted Guide to Santa Fe &
Vague Blueprint to the Cosmos

STAVO MUSTANG CRAFT

By The Muses Press

"Use Your Antenna....."

AUTO ANTENNA

SEQUENCE ONE

It's the kind of place that calls to you, like Zeus calling you to Mount Olympus. A personal invitation from the gods. A state with the words "Land of Enchantment" inscribed on every license plate... I kept my doubts right in front of me, at first, like the steering wheel guiding me toward my destiny. But the doubt faded with each sunset, if one were to calculate time in such a way. Three sunsets to be exact, by then I was drawn in and hooked. Not by an opportunity, or a person —I didn't really know anyone here— but called to the land itself; a talisman of place and sky.

I dreamt of it before I ever stepped foot in it. The strong vivid dreams that wake you. There I was walking down a street when suddenly everyone started floating in waves, psychedelic apparitions, defying physical logic. But no one panicked or even reacted. I was to understand that this is just how things were here, a paradise built as much upon mindwaves as sun-dried clay, sand, and straw. "Where IS this?" I thought. It needed a name to root it in something beyond the nebulous charms of fantasy. I looked to my left and saw a plaque against an adobe wall with the words "Santa Fe, New Mexico" written in script. Though now that I am acquainted with the city, locals often rightly call it "Fanta Se." I awoke with a startle in a bed in Tennessee, but with a clear prescient directive to travel west. And now I even know which street I was on in that dream, exactly where I was standing. Which is strange if you're not disposed to believing in precognition. I had never been here, but clearly I already knew the body of its mapping intimately.

1

I'm tempted to assert that Santa Fe is not exactly a literal city, but somehow a Goddess, a living thing, using light and long shadows, to take physical form and to call those to it, or turn those away, that it requires; to breath its intended energies and subtle hues of desert magic into this mystique-starved planet. Just a tiny corner of the world, but if you consider that even after centuries of investigation of the human vessel, scientists continue to discover new parts of the body each year, then clearly it follows that there are lots of small places in existence that still hold huge mysteries. Even with the benefit of our x-ray enhanced vision and penchant for big mouths, scientists just this week discovered a new muscle critical for chewing. This reveals both the astounding twists and turns of the collective human race in its long unfolding process of becoming, and the arresting limits of our scientific achievement even after two million years since first experimenting with tools. Whatever its age, Santa Fe works like a tiny slightly opened window at the top of a castle, that draws in a microscopic but continuous stream of the mysterious and esoteric. Not to mention that it does so with a host of intoxicating fragrances.

Artists and radical individualists have been attracted to what calls itself the City Different for over a century. To reinvent themselves, reenvision their lives, recover a past they didn't actually live but maybe should have, and right the path of personal history. No, it's not too late! "It is always beginning" could just as well be the mantra across New Mexico license plates. The second chance you're not supposed to get, that is if the universe was truly cold, unfeeling, and remote, the way the scientists who write the textbooks would like us to believe. Not for any bad reason, they just don't know any better.

I first arrived on the 4th of April in my sky blue 1959 Ford Galaxie Victoria. This precious stainless-steel hunk is something I already owned, pre-dating my fascination with Santa Fe and the statewide marketing campaign around the acquisition of turquoise, the mining for which goes back to prehistoric times. The oldest mine of any kind in North America is right here in Santa Fe County, and the turquoise excavated here is the only variety formed out of a volcano. So yes, that central character in the story, my pastel-hued companion, was like a chess piece already in place, way ahead of any awareness that my life was taking a turn toward the turquoise capital. Precursors of that sort materialize often here, like meeting someone at a party you had almost decided not to attend, and going to see a house to rent the next day, and having that same person greet you at the door, a representative for the landlord.

"How much is the rent?" I said to Sophia the agent, the latest messenger of transformation. Someone scuttles by me with a vase of hollyhocks and sets them on the table, still putting elements of homey comfort in place, as if I were dreaming it into being as the moment unfolds. Turns out, it would cost half of what I had paid in any other city I've lived in, with far more visual appeal. I hand her the application.

"We have so many people coming to see it today," Sophia says. "But I think I can tell you, you're at the top of the list" and she winks at me. Still, I almost missed my chance. Having not heard back after two weeks, I had a lease to another place ready and printed for me to sign, which I had put off for some reason until the very end of the day. Finally I asked myself "What are you waiting for?" and picked up the pen to officialize it. Just as I did, the phone rang and I stared with surprise that the caller ID said 'Sophia'... She offered me the place just as I was about to commit to something else. Five years later, I'm still gleefully enjoying the location.

A state doesn't get to be called the Land of Enchantment without more than just a few brushes with some strange and witchy happenings in its historical repertoire. Like, that shapeshifting dream I had in advance of arriving was not the only hint about this city being on my destiny's radar. Just days before my first visit, I was contacted out of the blue by a friend I hadn't heard from in ten years sending me an email to reconnect, which included photographs from his recent adventures. And having no idea about the trip I was about to embark on, the very first thing I see as the photos download is 'S A N T A F E' as it scrolled down with his picture featuring the historic Santa Fe Railyard Depot. "Oh, but it's an old dusty city, no place of magic," some might think on the surface, and believe furthermore that such fate-kissed precursors are of course no more than random coincidence. Until they occur with such stunning

3

exactness and synchronicity, that you'd be taking a bigger leap of faith to discount them, than to embrace a larger arc of possibility.

I drive into town, not knowing where the road will take me. A powder blue scarf that matches Esmeralda, the car. I've stitched some pieces of patterned fabric into my blouse, and have got a yellow skirt on because, today, my lower regions are definitely aligned with the power of the sun. My hips are moving to the music as I drive, free of the constraining force of any seatbelt, while my arms occasionally lift off the steering wheel to the rhythm. Visual portrait of a girl as a free man. I've embroidered some red stitching down the side of the skirt to draw attention to the thread-like nature of clothing. But it's about the way we stitch ourselves together with a little of this energy, a little of that experience, or this subtle influence, or that various half-belief. And always in our personalities, with visible loose threads dangling about, as we are always unfinished and in motion.

  RADIO REPORT: —Blondie's "Pretty Baby"— plays. I look in the rearview mirror and peek over my sunglasses. The breeze is light, and the ambience of the early day, an apparitional stranger one could so easily get wrapped up in. I push the pedal down and am carried forward.

Even on the verge of my sixth decade, I am still in touch with all that is splendiloquent in a six-year-old, vivacious in spirit with those solar powers of creation intact and the concurrent bringing forth of light that results. I keep my hair blonde, shaped in a cresting wave circling above the eye, to suggest suspending movement even in perfect stillness, as the radio fills the air with sonic waves that go by my fancifully accessorized earlobe, with a dangling diamond cloud.

By profession, I'm what you might call a theracoach, a combination of therapist and life coach. My business card reads 'Human Potential Advocate' but these are just words. Basically, I help people reach for the heights of their personal potential. It's taken years of study to identify what permits certain people to excel and enter the realm of the exceptional, and what psychological boundaries must be broken to penetrate such a rarified space. And perhaps even the way I deal with threads in my clothing is part of some elemental practice for teaching my mind how to identify the threads in a person's psychology; to see the patterns that connect their life choices and stories into a tapestry. Being in the consciousness business, dynamics of thought and energetics of the mind are fascinating to me.

Some very wild ideas that mystics had intuited thousands of years ago do often find themselves supported by science, which eventually catches up to, and sometimes surpasses, the weird outlandish original concepts. The discoveries of quantum physics, for instance, suggest that the stories of our wildest imagination are not merely the stuff of dreaming, but deeper layers of fact; of worlds living in the unseen. That all these things that seem separate to us —the chair, the wall, your arm— are actually all connected, with photons and electrons dancing right through both the living and inorganic matter, as one continuous energy field, and that what your eyes were firmly telling you was fact, was an elemental mirage.

Few of us drink water and think "I am ingesting Hydrogen and Oxygen" and of course, there are countless things in our realities that have a definitive appearance, but which are actually composed of a number of hidden and unaccounted for variables. The illusions envelope us everywhere! Even our everyday use of the internet is an example of appearances entirely overshadowing the real structure of things. The pages we surf look one way, but they are constructed behind the scenes using HTML, CSS and scripts. The color on the screen we see as blue is just a numeric formula: hex code #0000FF.

We may also tend to think we are our age, but many of the particles that make up the cells in your body have actually existed for millions of millennia. We are made of exploded star matter. (But I know, you think you are nothing special. You, this ordinary beast!)

An aggressive current of wind darts a large surprise tumbleweed across the road toward the front of the car, causing me to swerve slightly to avoid its prickly encroachment, while two ravens also lift off the ground, as if dashing from a predator. Their bodies huge in solidity to

5

whatever you imagine a bird of their size would need to take flight, they are nothing like what we see in paintings, as their smaller cousins the crow are what is usually depicted, precisely because their compact size is more convenient to visual scale on a canvas. You can't help notice the formidable beak of the raven, and their thick meaty bodies, even seen at a distance. Their black color and scavenger diets have long made them associated with death, but these clever talkative creatures feel closer to realms of prophecy and insight than to the barren world of the cataclysmic, and their blackness more indicative of inhabiting the mysterious with native comfort, rather than the inertness and finality of the unliving.

I see my new neighbor Joss drive by in the opposite direction, heading toward our casitas as we wave. One of the wonderful things about Santa Fe is the intimacy of it. I met the DJ on one of the big local stations I love to listen to, and now I can just text him and he plays my request over the radio, and says, "This song goes out to Cybilline in Santa Fe!" You smile pretty wide when that happens. Coming from big cities where everything is the cold machine, it's something special to end up in a place where you find it isn't.

And it's not just that things aren't what they seem, but that our minds aren't either.

We tend to think ideas just come from our brains, but what about how artists often speak of muses, just "energies" that they interact with as a co-creator of their art, that guides them but also teaches them unexpected nuggets and reflections, arriving at unanticipated illuminations. What if consciousness just EXISTS, and rather than being a pure product of our minds, is a free-flowing signal our brains simply tap into. And what if human minds aren't actually that great at doing so, and are more equivalent to a cheap transistor radio, and that there are entities out there in the universe with boom boxes for processors, connecting and broadcasting at a much more dynamic level.

We accept a phrase like "I Think Therefore I Am" as proof of existence. But it would seem to follow that "*I Communicate Therefore I Am*" would also be a signifier; that if the universe can talk to us, whether that's through synchronicities, unlikely coincidence, strange callings, "signs" we receive, as when we say "the universe is trying to tell me something", it means the universe is conscious.

And why should that be a strange idea? Consciousness existing outside of the human mind is no different a concept really than how electricity is not confined to the electric sockets in our homes, but also operates throughout our body when we move our muscles or think a thought, without needing to 'plug in' someplace; electricity manifestly exists all over. We have simply learned how to tap into it.

So when I say that people re-invent themselves in Santa Fe, I really mean people are tapping into a recognition of an already present potential that rises to the surface. A lot of random things in your life, like the town you grew up in, the assumptions that abound there about gender and profession and finance, the coping mechanisms you apply to early challenges, which qualities of personality seem to bring approval, all begin to become solidified as habit... They all conspire to tell you who you are, based on comfort zones established by an array of externally-determined conditions thrust upon you. But our ideas about who we are often prevent us from even trying activities and directions that contradict this original script. What become core identity structures could have been written into us, like any fiction novel, based merely on conveniences and routine; good old fashioned inertia. It could be a certain type of joke that you would tell with your parents, that brought you a sense of belonging and connection to their love, but a humor whose sensibilities actually have nothing to do with how you, in your core, see the world. That love and approval caused you to perpetuate a ghost, to dress it up and teach it how to talk with a foreign vocabulary. But one with fairly random characteristics, you might mistake for a Person! A person with your name.

We spend many formative years growing from the inside out, but one technology of consciousness is to explore the material of the external, and bring it inward. The outside-in model can also be fun, like attending a wild dress-up party. It takes a while in life to see you are wearing many costumes inside yourself as much as you wear them on the outside. Without any conscious awareness, people often "perform" their ideas about race, gender, age, sexuality, even nationality. Identity aspects we take on from external perceptions, rather than from internal impulse, mistaking our allegiance to team characteristics for our true inner individual sensibilities. But it's just acting. Borrowing totems of belonging and over-identifying with it as a shortcut to a sense of self.

This is why Salvador Dali places huge crutches in his paintings, perhaps most humorously affected in his "*The Burning Giraffe, 1937*", where drawers are used to represent the hiding places of the unconscious. The crutches illustrate psychological apparatus we lean upon to build our identity. But Dali is sympathetic to the human animal, as —crutches as they may be— we somehow still do take effective action from these precarious positions. We build a cohesive narrative from those half-baked stories we tell ourselves, and of course the crutches are not just affectation, they're necessary support structures.

My cell phone rings and as I keep my eye most intently upon the road, I tip it to a full 45-degree angle, and quickly catch a glance that it's just tonight's restaurant verifying my reservation. If they only knew, my selections from the menu are already being placed in my mind, with all that impending flavor as a quiet atmospheric accoutrement to my day, up until the moment I arrive. I will definitely show up and I will be a sight to behold.

The Japanese term Geisha has an interesting etymology, which is gei (art) and sha (person)... literally, an art person. Most people think artists just make things, but I've always felt Being Your Own Highest Artform was the real purpose of art, and not necessarily what you craft to leave behind. The former clearly carries the grander evolutionary trajectory. And no matter how much people like to say their art will outlive them, your soul will far outlive it all. So that's the thing to invest in.

  RADIO REPORT: — "JEWELS & FUR" BY GALACTIC WITCHCRAFT— PLAYS.

The car shifts gears, and the engine purrs with inclined strength and the grace of innovation, which even having sixty years of distance for advancement, has not been improved upon, it seems. Certainly not in style. Not in enjoyment.

Not in pride of ownership. Gas mileage has improved. One step forward, yet many steps back.

This is why my position on humanity is that it's not distinguishably improving. That even that storyline of linear advancement is a red herring in the understanding of our purpose. That we're, instead, in a back and forth shifting of gears with history, told over a minimum of the last 12,000 years since settling into farming communities. Despite many warp-jump breakthroughs along the way, not the least of which is hot running water, it's still a journey better understood as a collection of moments and assemblage, rather than rungs on the ladder in the great chain of being.

Let me tell you about a really brilliant Siamese cat I had the pleasure of living my life with for a time. Her name was Babette. Part of what separates human development from most other animals is the ability to think in symbols. Poetry, you might say, is what separates us. Usually animals look at your finger when you point, and not where you are pointing at. That's called "eating the menu" instead of what the words represent. But Babette broke with evolutionary code by recognizing my finger was being used as a symbol to get her to look at an intended spot. That developed into my being able to just curl my index finger toward my palm, and her coming over to me without my saying a word.

Sure, she could open doors and play extended games of fetch, but she could also read people. She'd stare at them from across the room and size them up, and I learned to trust her assessment in how she would sometimes show trust toward someone that was otherwise very good at concealing their emotional character, at least to humans. She performed some mental tricks on dogs too. Babette would sit upright on my lap at the vet, because being in a cage was beneath her developmental level, and dogs would inevitably come in and start to dart at her. But with fearless unflinching calm, she remained still and seated fully upright like an Egyptian cat statue, the goddess Bastet, and communicated through action, 'I am not part of the dog chases cat paradigm' and everyone watched with some amazement, as by her not playing into the 'you big dog, I fearful cat' game, these dogs got the message and would sit down before her like a good boy, and allowed her to look upon them and lightly sniff the air, gathering god knows what other data on her now well-behaved and obedient new animal friends.

But she could still only be that which was CAT. In other words, however far she evolved and outpaced her contemporaries, there was a limit. She could still only be as genius as the biological limitations of cat could allow, and no more. The human animal is the same. And I won't go into all the interdimensional beings whose evolutionary development could make a housepet of the human mind, and its comparatively meager capacities. Just as reference, mantis shrimp perceive the world through twelve channels of color, while humans process only three— blue, green and red. Imagine the impoverishment of perception! And I mean, sure you're impressed by all these wires over our streets, which carry electricity in rudimentary analog connection from home to home. The signs of modernity and advanced civilization, to US. But galactics who have ventured across the sea of the sky, traveling through waves of time, see these wires and immediately identify they are encountering a primitive state of technology, put in place by the wildly limited intellect of its host population.

 RADIO REPORT: — "MODERN TV" BY THE CLEANERS FROM VENUS— COMES BOOMING OVER THE SPEAKERS, WHILE I STARE UP AT A RED TRAFFIC LIGHT. FOOT TAPS.

And I know, to some, that sounds rich... Beings from other worlds? But let's understand a few basics of mental blockades in perception. If you're an ant, the idea of other worlds existing past the ocean is beyond comprehension. Clearly this literal line in the sand, this water, is the end of connection to Any Places Elsewhere. We hit a similar conceptual roadblock with a human brain to understand that other worlds across this galaxy and beyond, are still connected by unseen currents and waveforms, much like our rickety electric power lines, but along a far broader and more sophisticated grid. The limits are not of space but of our fragmented simple animal brains, which are just as they were 2,500

10

years ago in Ancient Greece and 2,500 years before that in Ancient Egypt.

Part of that archaic animal mind is still visible in our current psychological mirror when we consider the degree to which we are creatures of quite automated processing. We can pat ourselves on the back for being able to 'determine' what we're in the mood to eat for breakfast, and 'choose' to go to the place that serves that, and 'decide' what drink to have with it, after figuring out what we'll wear that day. But any of the mechanics of how your body actually digests that food, how you time the chewing and breathing, how your eyes stay hydrated by blinking, to how you get turned on by the shape of someone's body as they walk by and catch yourself staring at them. It's all involuntary. How you hear what someone says to you during that breakfast and how the signal is sent to your brain to interpret, entirely automated processes. That itch you scratch. You're being told what to do all day by signals outside of your conscious will. And even when at our best at channeling our energy with conscious intent, as in art, any great movie director will tell you, the best cinematic moments in their films were commonly a result of accident and pure kismet.

As I drive further down Agua Fria and feel the sun nibble on my flesh, my love for the intense dry heat against my skin felt through open car windows only increases. Living in the high desert, there are a number of cues of place you get used to, which speak to your cellular self as signifiers of home, and this is one of them. That dry warmth which never leaves you feeling soggy and unappetizing, but always penetrated and radiant. A mosquito-free summer existence, that's at least one less thing preying upon you in this world.

Yes, the birds and bees do it, and the trees do it. Animals basking in the life-giving rays of the sun is one of the simplest phenomena to explain. Tanned skin is not some modern image fetish, but actually a return to our natural innate color... the one we'd have without clothes. That primitive resonance is why it holds a carnal force in its appeal. And did you know that even elephants, with their bare hairless skin always revealed without any protection of fur, have almost no skin cancer? Maybe it's the degree to which we've removed ourselves from any natural order that has compromised us, because the occurrence of cellular replication errors among animals in the wild is very rare, with their cancers more commonly being a result of wounds or bites that fester. Admittedly they do use a mud bath as a native brand of suntan lotion, so there's one sterling vote of approval from nature on getting dirty. Apparently you either need a fur coat or a filth coat to survive this life.

But what really strikes me, having been kissed by the warmth most vociferously over these late days of Spring, is how I've often felt like I was not on Earth at all but on a celestial plane of timeless basking, with light flickering through the trees to my eyelids, hitting in a parade of insights, as if attending a lecture descendent from the stars... And of particular note, a profound lack of need for any activity other than Being— an inert state without wants and full of contentment, as if traveling the whole world from the confines of my enclosed patio.

I make a right turn into Frenchy's Park, observing the elegant shape of the steering wheel as it spins, and parking carefully, shutting down the motor. Another of those cues of place you come to recognize living in Santa Fe is the large population of prairie dogs. They're adorable. There are a number of areas where they've truly made themselves a home here, Frenchy's being one. More like prayer than prairie, in how they really do sit up with their fingers touching in an upright worshipful stance, while emitting a playful joy, reminiscent of Buddhic reverence, saluting the divinity in all.

Reaching behind the passenger seat, I grab an old painted wooden flute and step outside. Walking past the playground and the spiral labyrinth, a circular path constructed to encourage people to slow down and be patient and eschew distraction, I face the field with so many visible pockets leading to the underground worlds of Santa Fe's favorite burrowing rodents.

When I play a few notes, three have popped their heads out, and after a few more moments, their curiosity heightens and two come a bit closer, to inspect. They look at each other and look back over at me. Is it strange how music unites across animal and plant sentience, or is this just a cosmic clue about an underlying vibrational foundation that forms the physical world itself, which all living beings naturally harmonize with?

My little concert is quickly done, with my command over wooden flute notes being rudimentary at best, and I hear them making their high-pitched jovial noises under the ground as I walk along the path above them, a kind of continuation of environmental music. It's clear why they are well-liked, and thinking about how Santa Fe means "Holy Faith" and the prayer-like stances these creatures adopt, it's perfect symmetry that they should be protected here. I was told once that to have permission to even *move* them from their dwellings, you must hand wash them and hand feed them, and only with that level of commitment to their wellbeing, could you legally relocate them. And well, that degree of detail is likely a bit of lyrical fiction. But it meanwhile avails us a peeping view into the minds of those other playful and unconventional creatures of local habitation: those who have put such an ordinance of protection in place, the modern-day Santa Fean.

The breeze caresses my hair and finds an opening through the tresses. I place my finger to the top of my ear and trace back along the ridge to tuck in wayward strands. And suddenly I decide to ignore the pathway laid down by city planners for people to walk upon, and instead go in the direction dictated only by the sun. I walk into the uncut grass and follow that stream of light forward. And as I break free of the confinement of rules and expectation —on where to walk, on which direction to take— I come across two butterflies encircling each other and rising up into the sky above my head. Which I never would have encountered had I not strayed from that pre-set stone trail. And just one in a lifelong string of reminders to get off other people's paths, and go follow my own.

SEQUENCE TWO

Depending on your perspective of time, it was not so long ago that we ourselves may have crept out of the oceans, with webbed claw for foot, grabbing by storm that rare fleeting motivation to transcend the pleasures of idleness, and rushing to land, that would embark a whole new trajectory for the human species. One that may still yet lead to the stars. But I have other theories...

I am not so much interested in the collective as I am in individual will. There is one type of spiritualist always concerned with gatherings and holding hands. I am more fascinated by the first person who opted to come out of the water toward land. Having very little faith in group thinking, I carry a tremendous belief in the potential of individuals walking their lone road.

As such, I frequently dine by myself. I enjoy the sensation of occupying a Table for Four while sitting with the majestic grace of a Party of One. A Siamese cat as a girl, always at home wherever she sits, with elegant posture and eyes that scan the room with a regal countenance. I eroticize being alone. There is still some taboo against doing this, as well as against going to movies alone, another of my favorite pastimes. Or in certain religious sects, a taboo against self-pleasure. Or any pleasure. But frankly, there is also a certain taboo against believing in yourself and allowing your life to have meaning beyond the paycheck you receive. There is a taboo against keeping your own place even if married or fervently coupled, but I also believe in that. Sleeping alone is sublime in my lush satin sheets— can that be wrong? But in that instance, I'm known to bend the rules. It's so important for any kitty to purr.

I reach the center of town with my reservation for one, at the city's most beloved Italian bistro for those with taste, Andiamo. At the arrival of the first dish, a delectable crispy polenta with a generous helping of rosemary gorgonzola sauce that makes even the blandness of polenta taste dynamically flavorful, I make eye contact with another lone diner. He was positioned in the opposite corner of the restaurant, with our chairs faced just enough towards each other that any natural gaze forward would require consciously looking away to not appear staring. So I glance over to my left and note the mechanical ruler splayed on the wall as decor. Which is actually a pretty high understanding of art, to identify its inherent charm as wall-worthy. Duchamp would be proud. And let's not forget, the entire art of cuisine is based on measurements.

The waitress brings the glass of dessert wine I like to start with, a toe-curling Ben Rye... After all, why wait for the end of a meal and a full stomach to begin the festivities of pleasure? And when my eyes lower from thanking the waitress, I see I am being watched. I don't at all shy from what quickly moves from a light glance to the extended starring where pupils lock coordinates, which —once you've gotten that familiar with the inner gears of another's ocular motors— can rapidly evolve from visual grazing into all out eye-fucking.

I can't help but note under his cowboy hat is a good set of lookers.

This is precisely why I don't understand people who bemoan being single. Living in a perpetual state of potential romance not good enough for you? But I admit, as dining alone goes, it's fairly rare to encounter a fellow outlier. Though that solitary act itself suggests a healthy penchant for finding sustainment in observation, a prized trait.

As this fetching lone wolf dips his bread in the virgin olive oil, I delicately fork the crispy polenta and take a bite smothered in gorgonzola, and make a subtle sigh to indicate my receptivity of being pleased, by this dish— just audible enough that when I do glance over, he looks down at his oil-drenched bread, but then quickly back up to see if I return his serve. Which I do, and then lightly lift my paper menu, allowing it to limply dangle elegantly over my finger, as I peek at the entrees, pretending to not know every detail of what's transcribed therein.

"Cybilline-on-the-scene!" the waiter Cisco says in rhyme, which I'm glad of because I really didn't want to keep up the reading act, and the sooner he tells me the specials, the sooner I can reject those, for what I came to the restaurant knowing in advance that I wanted to enjoy. Of course I explore menus like any good bird of prey, but I also like to make the whole city a roving buffet, and having identified what each restaurant does best, I can choose where to go based on what specific dish I'm in the mood for. The selection is usually made before I open the car door.

"It's so good to see you back. I see you've already gotten your favorite appetizer," he smiles with recognition of my frequent visits. "Would you like to hear the specials?" "You know I would," I insincerely assure with enthusiasm. And after I've ordered the regular, my favorite chicken parmigiana anywhere, he says, "I'll bring you your Blue Sky ginger ale." I love that he does that without my needing to ask, because it is the best brand of ginger ale, and it was one of those products that originally developed out of the back of a truck in Sante Fe. I feel the treasure of this lore when I sip it, with that most perfect blend of sweet and tangy ginger taste. Now, of course, it's since become owned by Coca-Cola, but the formula is the same, and it generally takes the place of water for me at Andiamo where they still carry it for its local roots.

For the moment, I do gulp one swig of water as I wait. Living in the high desert you could not even be aware you were thirsty at all, take a random sip and that dose of moisture feels like it's literally saving your life. The tastiest water in the world is that which enters a thirsty mouth. Though, as I've always been one for turning water into wine, I quickly return to my Ben Rye and stare contemplatively ahead, before allowing my sight to wander just to the right, where a potential protagonist is now studying the menu instead of looking unceasingly over here. But I can wait.

There's something so interesting in the mating rituals of many animals, and not just us mammals; the awkward body movements and strange noises that emit from the throat, for instance, but also how the boys instead of girls often perform the colorful ritual dances to entice. The peacock spider is a riot. In the case of a tarantula, he encounters white silken thread left by the female, like a strewn path of undies and other sultry remains, then he taps a rhythm on her layer and she taps back to indicate readiness... and if when she emerges, he doesn't catch her fancy, she eats him. For the record, I am nowhere near that high maintenance.

It's only by nearly the end of the meal that my silken threads are put on display, in the form of my statement, "Oh yes I would love dessert!" This signifies a closing of the window of opportunity as well as indicating readiness for a delivery of sweets. The male in this instance makes his case.

He's gotten up from his chair. "I hope this isn't a bother, but you seem so intriguing sitting here, I was hoping you would allow me to come over and have dessert with you," he says, and adds after I don't immediately reply, "since we're both eating by ourselves." He's a little more handsome up close, his cheekbones chiseled like an editorial model, and eyes green instead of brown, the way they appeared from across the room under the shadow of his hat. Eyes that are somewhat guarded in their expression but nothing hinting at alarm in the slightest. "The name is Gunner."

"I guess I wouldn't mind." Cards played. "Kind of you to offer, I'm Cybilline," and I blink twice and smile— allowing an accruing of interest before encountering the actual energy exchange of the flesh that a handshake might ignite. "Your clothes are so unique, I can't help but wonder if you're a famous designer," he pries. "I'm not a famous anything," I assure him, "I design for myself." I lift my sleeve to reveal threads of cloth stitched over the original blouse fabric, and watch him eye the details. "It's called upcycling; I just sew on bits and pieces, really."

Upcycling is a phenomenon of arting up the self and playfully indulging in thrift store fascination that actually found its roots in Santa Fe and Taos. While the initial modern incarnation of the impulse may be traced to late 70s British punks and the embellishment and adornment of ripped clothing, the new mindful couture of Santa Fe's Recycle Art Market and Runway Trash Fashion Show goes back 25 years, as the country's largest and oldest market of its kind. With its wearable art of repurposed fabric reapplications, the upcycling phenomenon was a delicious part of my initiation into the blissful Santafecation of my existence. My attire reveals many things, among them the secrets of occasional pattern clashing and the lost succulent joys of texture ritual. These are things not all sentient beings can register as meaningful however, and so I watch the eyes of others as they behold, for signs of comprehension.

There's a moment of unspoken recognition that we're both talking to discuss topics but also not topics; a private eye detection exchange. That's a badge you should never give up. Flirting keeps your spirit effervescent and keen, a candle flickering in the furnace of the heart— but just as with window shopping, it's often more fun considering possibilities than bringing the merchandise home— or even looking at the price tag.

Either way, once he sat down, the other side of the table looked better with him there than not. Eating the male, still not out of the question. The fingers on my right hand tap across the table twice in the rhythmic chant of the hungry desert tarantula.

"Cybilline, is the gentleman joining you?" Cisco is quick to manage his tables, but stands-in as a watchful protector, to be certain I'm comfortable but also making sure this guy is fully aware that he knows The Tarantula Lady. "I'd like for dessert to be on my tab," Gunner says before I can even reply, while he points back over to his table. "Oh now that's really not necessary!" I say, still feeling out the situation. "Well I've invited myself, it's the least I can do," he says, eyebrows expressively raised.

Cisco looks at me. "It's fine," I tell him, then look back to my new friend, and thank him. He places a small journal on the table, and I quickly exhale in recognition, and lift my diary out of my pea green bag with soft leather pockets. I like to catalog things, discoveries I make in exploring the world. I write a little about them in these journals and make drawings which somehow creates longer legs of personalization, connecting me more viscerally to a topic, making my memory of it more the way an event is processed, instead of just an object. "So what've you got there?" I inquire, eyeing toward Gunner's notebook.

"Oh, I'm actually helping to compile a book of celebrity interviews, just a side hustle."

"The Santa Fe Shuffle," we both say in unison, and laugh. Because there are very few sustaining jobs in Santa Fe, it is extremely common for people to grab two or three shifting gigs to cover expenses, and that's referred to as the Santa Fe Shuffle, a survival-based kind of dance move, performed to the beat of necessity. There's an old joke about the lack of opportunity to make money in this town, that goes "How do you leave Santa Fe with a million dollars?"

"Arrive with two million."

It turns out that Gunner is here for a few weeks delivering art for a show at a new gallery opening, so he's in and out of town regularly. It's astounding but we have just about one quarter the amount of art galleries as a mecca like New York City does, but placed in context of the latter possessing over a hundred times our population, this tells you just why Santa Fe has more artists per capita than anywhere else in America, if not the world. The result is that a city of only 75,000 people is the third largest art market in the country, based on sheer volume of sales from flea antique to fine art, in large part owed to the huge transplant population drawn here by that abidingly accurate mythology of a land that miraculously inspires people to produce the best work of their lives. While New York and Los Angeles have very practical reasons that magnetize artists to their shores, the calling to this desert town has to do with being drawn by the allure of something deeper. Specifically, mystery.

I have to admit I didn't peg the cowboy for an art enthusiast, though granted he may not be— He might just have the hands for it.

But I'm curious about the side hustle. "So what kind of celebrities exactly? Actors, singers?" I inquire and he nods. My eyes squint and mimic search to see what I'm missing, "So... what topics do these dramatists specialize in, to keep a reader's attention glued for a whole book?"

Despite the social accolades that accompany being a 'name', there's nothing particularly more special or valid about a celebrity opinion than that of your next-door neighbor, and I always hold hope that people can generally identify that. Chances are considerably higher in fact that your neighbor in any mildly cosmopolitan area has more interesting views, in part because they are allowed to air honest perspectives, without worrying that their opinions will make them unpopular and cast a shadow on obtaining future roles. Since they are not part of a market selling brands, your ordinary neighbor will not have consulted with a legal team and an image maker before speaking, and won't comfortably present in caricature. Yet the public actually wants to know who such people are dating... what they "said" or did... in lifestyles so often arranged for them, to publicly perform, by a publicist or manager. Not entirely different than a puppy being groomed and walked for a show. No joke! But as the spell of stardom seems not to wane, it appears that people prefer fantasies, a fact which Freud would not have been at all surprised by. "I told you so," he nods from behind the pages of every one of his manuscripts, with smoke from his pipe emitting white-magic clouds.

"What topics? Speaking about nothing but themselves, I imagine. But I just love all the celebrity gossip," he shrugs. "Maybe because of the magazines my mom used to bring home from the grocery," he says, unconsciously rubbing his finger under his nose, "you know, all those behind-the-scenes stories, I love the big reveal."

"You know actors fabricate reality for a living, right?" I tease. "You ever think about how we can become attached to a character in a film and yet the actor whose poster is on the wall didn't choose any of those words coming out of their mouth, or the clothes their character wears. A writer or director, I can understand having a greater interest in, but the actors are a bit like the cheerleaders, not the quarterback; they're not where the real action generates from."

He shifts in his chair thoughtfully, and with one eye half-squinting says, "What would a casting director say to that?"

"They'd say, 'True but I still have to pick the right cheerleader,'" I quip back.

"OK," he concedes smiling, "but you must sometimes read rags like People Magazine? Don't you appreciate the whole star system on some level," unfolding his napkin in preparation for the dessert arriving. Damn it if the waitress at just that moment doesn't walk by with our order, but then delivers those same dishes to another table.

Now he's hitting on a worthy topic. There actually are magnificent light shows that project across dark space from the staggering interaction of solar winds dynamically pulling against the galaxy's magnetic fields; cosmic rays that bounce off space gas and dust, which produce astounding sculpted shapes in the most intricate spectral lines!

The evolution of the universe is itself a kind of beauty conversation across space. And frankly, the offerings on Earth by comparison, are fairly muted... Imagine living instead on a planet with multiple moons, where not all the orbs are dead; where you might travel to the third moon of Planet Quasar, the same way one might travel to the beaches of Puerto Vallarta, on the Pacific coast of Mexico, for just a quick getaway. For comparison, Jupiter has over 70 moons. Earth is like that small town that exists way off the map from compelling destinations, that even other small towns don't really bother mentioning. Or a bland restaurant down a long deserted bumpy road. And while that town thinks its quaint County Fair is the most spectacularly engrossing thriller of an event anywhere, it's quite a dud to any unsleeping eye.

Even to try to defend our dear little blue marble against such statements of fact is a small-town impulse, I'm afraid; clinging to the safety that the codifiable simplicity of scarcity and limitation provide, not being able to fathom an ever-multiplying plethora of wonders, which far transcends what your little town offers. To doubt the magnificent abundance and diversity that richly await in other worlds, including realms where even some of the creatures believed to be mythological reside (just because those entities have little interest in incarnating in the physical environs of Earth, which is not a sign they don't exist, but only solidifies their staggering claim to unbridled cool!) is a sad folly indeed... Luckily the universe has such astounding grace that we still have plenty of breathtaking phenomena and magical creatures to provide a lifetime of engagement and investigation. I mean, the two-legged specimen sitting right here across my table fairly fits that category, so I'm not exactly taking issue.

"To tell you the truth, Gunner... I've often thought if I ever got the opportunity to create a magazine, it would be the opposite of People." He smiles and leans back in his chair, starting to stroke that chin somewhat. "It would be called 'Nobody Magazine' and feature all the people out there in the world doing amazing things, completely off the radar of prying eyes. Little pockets of scenes, without necessarily even mentioning where it's happening, but just THAT it's happening."

"Like your upcycling thing here," he says, pointing at my rather fine stitching, possibly trying to draw attention to his masculinely dry and cracked but dynamically formed fingers. But I will not be distracted by the parading of male charms. "Yes, exactly," I reply with appreciation for his astuteness, and only minor awareness of the truly exceptional golden facial ratios of eyes-to-mouth proximity he possesses. "Or this guy from Amsterdam, Viktor IV, spelled with the Roman IV but pronounced four, who changed his name four times and lived on a boat, where he created these painted wooden icons that people in the city accepted as cash, to honor the largeness of his spirit. Or the skaters in Berlin's abandoned airport, where the plane runways have been repurposed as a huge public gathering party space, where human joy lifts off instead of aircrafts." He smiles and twists his leather bracelet, more seemingly as a comfort than adjustment of size. "Or just this wrench jockey who lives up the street from me," I say gesticulating with my arm, "who mixed and matched classic body kits to build an incredibly astounding car, all by himself, that makes me laugh every time he drives by. A singular person with a car no one else in the world has! I love it." He nods his head in appreciation, and a detectable lilt is in his smile.

Finally our desserts are delivered. The profiteroles are amazing and I am looking forward to that first bite. I can't help but appreciate that he ordered Tiramisu. There's no specific correlation, but it seems somehow a soft sensitive dessert for him. I mean, soaked ladyfingers? I would've guessed a muddy Pot De Creme for sure. He slowly pops his spoon into the dish and purposefully scrapes along the edge of the bowl.

"I get it," he gleams. "Just look at those Earthships developed out in Taos," he says, "that almost no one knows about, which let people live entirely off the grid, using old tires as insulation, repurposing materials that otherwise would have no way to be recycled, and," he points out, "they never again get a bill from the energy or oil companies."

"And isn't that way cooler than what some actress thinks about the environment?" I reply.

At that, Gunner chuckles and twice taps his wine glass with his fork to ring out that I have struck a chord. He smiles down at his glass with a charming wine-fueled light in his eyes. "I'm giving up this book" he says, and tosses it on the floor. The waitress approaches with a handful of plates just then, because you can always count on perfect timing from the universe, and he quickly grabs it back up and places two fingers to his temple in an apologetic salute as she walks by, then turns his attention back to me.

"Well I knew you were interesting," Gunner says, craning his neck to the table next to ours as their meal is placed down, and then leaning toward me to speak. "But that was the darndest rant I've heard over dinner snacks in quite some time." I laugh into my wine glass. He keeps looking over without any rush to move the energy of conversation anywhere in particular. The way a ranch cowboy spends hours watching the herd slowly graze on the grass across the field before ever needing to take action on corralling them to other pastures. "You know, I just want to point out, this Hollywood interview gig just fell into my lap from some of the art drops I made in Los Angeles to the right people's homes, I guess... but," he finally says, "it's a paying gig."

"Cheers to that!" I lift my glass. "Maybe you should write the introductory commentary," he says, and I titter on that one. I actually love the topic of how the cult of celebrity serves a similar function in the psyche as cults of religion, a secular pacifier, akin to Santa Claus for adults. The flying man in the red suit we outgrow, but celebrity worship, not so much. And that's because there is a need, a human impulse to deify something, to put something on a pedestal above us. It's the same instinct as the primeval need for inventing gods. And that impulse isn't entirely without merit, because it is also the mind's attempt to recognize that it's part of a larger world, of far greater significance than itself. Just as the gods were assigned constellations in the sky above Ancient Rome, Greece, and Egypt, we call today's Hollywood substitutes, "stars" even rating them from minor status to superstars. And as the world becomes more and more unreligious, the rise of the celebrity seems to increasingly take its place for expressing a heightened stature, providing an ideal. Reality stars have gained adjacent placement perhaps because their elevation requires no particular talent, which more people can relate to, while providing a god for worship that you might passively feel even superior to. What a rush of serotonin for the mortal ego!

Yes, there is not necessarily much special about a person who stands on stage singing, or a thespian on a TV show you've seen. But this does not lessen the fact that one of the more fascinating human realities, which cannot be said of any other animal on Earth, is that there are people who have existed in history, that —having never met them— become our "friends" through the way they've directed their creative energies, and thereby shared something of value in themselves, with us... That we are deeply personally moved by, even indebted to. Whether through paint, song, photography, fashion, film, architecture, or the written word, to connect with your own soul in a way that becomes a light of illumination for others, somehow proves that there is something worthy about the toil of our existence, and some essential beauty in it. That we've come into being to do something important, even if entirely unrecognized.

That, set against the backdrop of the fact that more people watch the Superbowl in this country than an entire year's worth of PBS Nature. The desire for profound understanding about the workings of existence itself, versus viewing grown men chasing a ball.

"One thing I will suggest," Gunner says with a thoughtful pause as our desserts are finally reaching their final bites, "and this is just a theory here— but maybe a lot of people don't have particularly interesting lives, or they've been saddled by circumstance," he says. "And they're tired from just surviving and getting by, and they don't know how to dream of a different life. So they let those Hollywood gods, as it were, live a glamorous dream and they believe in it... even if it's a myth. They feel part of something. And they find reality in the stories."

"You know how Woody Allen always gets the girls in all those movies?" I ask.

"Yeah, how?"

"He wrote those movies."

Gunner and I step out of Andiamo together and catch the tail end of a sunset hovering over the Railyard. Inspiring as the colors are to stay mesmerized by, he's got to go meet his buddies over on Canyon Road who are installing a show tonight and I let him know I'll try to make the opening on Friday.

"I hope I see you around Cybilline," he calls over to me, "you're a real spark in the night, you know that?" he says, holding that stillness in his stance that belies an attractive degree of self-possession. "I'm sure we will," I call back. "Catch me on Instagram, *BeingCybilline*." I hold up my phone. "We can stay in touch."

It's not unlikely to have the pleasure of meeting again. In a quaint town like Santa Fe, you often do. It's a city where people will talk to you in restaurants and have insightful conversations, and maybe not ever see them again— or you just see them the next day at the post office. As I'm driving home to my casita, I think how the transience of things has never meant those experiences disappear. We store the aura of the most temporary connections somewhere in our energetic field. Maybe the reason so many go through such a variety of jobs and move through so many social worlds throughout life, is that we are sprinkling our soul mitochondria into those we intersect with, and both our casual and heavy connections are an astral kinetic force, a tide, that in some miniscule way fuels the solar winds and magnetic fields of the cosmos, a form of propellent that facilitates the spinning of the planets. That the purpose of our interactions in the microcosm, along with countless conscious galactic beings everywhere, is meager and insignificant compared to the unknown purposes set in motion in the distance of space.

I sit on my bed and touch a few crystals I picked up in town, which I've put on the nightstand. I know... Santa Fe is known for the crystal-waving ladies in parking lots, but that doesn't change that some people really can feel the vibrations of things. This exchange of energy is why you can sometimes receive more information about a person by touching their arm for just a moment, than from reading a 10-page interview.

Energy is everything, or so Einstein wrote. We generate electrical fields whenever we move our muscles, and there is enough electricity in our brains to produce little sparks of light all across the Earth. Our poetry is a different illumination, produced from non-electrical sources, but still one full of glint and flicker.

I open the jar by my bedside, and like all other nights, disperse my particles. If you were there, you'd see it— a molecular flow into this glass jar that becomes filled with 59 fireflies, and there's netting at the top. Until morning, when —energy recharged— a hand comes and opens the jar to set those fireflies free to reconfigure back into this earthly realm.

SEQUENCE THREE

I turn the key to start up Esmeralda, ready to surveil the surrounding areas. "Come on old girl..." Sometimes I can tell if she's going to be sluggish right out of the gate. I don't want to say automobiles, being machines, have moods... wheeled cyborgs that they are. But sometimes she runs so smooth and strong, and ready to take on any challenge asked. Then other days, it's "Where are you taking me, I'm tired. There must be a show on Netflix you meant to stream."

  RADIO REPORT: — "STRANGE POWERS" BY THE MAGNETIC FIELDS— PLAYS.

Driving down the dirt road heading out to the main street is strangely comforting, each bump a reminder that you're further out of those fully manicured social contracts of bigger cities. A little more like horseback, a little less like highway. I like the feel of the road under my wheels. I even like the soil kicking up a fine mist into the air; it doesn't feel like dirt. It feels like movement.

When you're surrounded by the county's high desert conditions, the desire to get out onto the cracked clay-like land is strong. While there's a national forest just seven minutes from the center of town in Santa Fe, it's a little less arid there. The easiest access to walking in wide open desert terrain is the Frank Ortiz Dog Park, a 1.4-mile loop trail and well over a hundred acres of arroyos and walkways, little birds, big birds, jack rabbits... and breathtaking views of the Jemez mountains and a look-out over the city. I don't have a dog but I have legs, eyes, nose. The smells of the scrub cedar, juniper, and minty cholla cactus far outweigh the potential fragrance of doggy doo. I embrace those odds.

Tina and Jacy are a couple, with the most adorable Shiloh Shepherd, he's such a big boy and cuddle wolf— and I see them often here. Another perk to the dog park is getting your canine fun in without having to pick up the brown bags and their contents. Kind of like visiting other people's kids... A colorful blast of play and silly— but they get to deal with the kicking and screaming. My top two finest and most critical life choices: not marrying, not having kids. It has helped to keep me preserved, saved from being neutralized, and a permission to remain at some level unserious, a condition many others are fooled into worshiping by their acute exposure to survival tensions, irrationally magnified by parenthood. From a mother's role of neurotic worry and over-protect, very few ever recover their risk-ready and carefree glory of girlhood. Many-a-mother exclaims, "You don't know what you missed!" but of course they'll never know the daring life of liberty they missed out on either.

Half-trotting over toward me, Tina is being dragged by Rolf, who by now recognizes me as his never-say-no friend. Because I'm never in a position to have to say no, but Rolf doesn't think that though. To him, it's all magic. His tail wags powerfully, his tongue full of wet sloppy love.

Rolf's humans are both artists and I occasionally get to counsel them, at no charge, on the various neurosis and ego insecurities most young artists struggle with. I had originally met them on the open artist studio tours that happen at the end of summer, across five weekends in a row —from Galisteo, to Abiquiu, the High Road to Taos, and the tour covering the territories of Madrid and Cerrillos— where you see the works people are making in all those adobe homes that dot the hills, but just as importantly, the magical way they are living. It was on that latter leg of the open studio weekends that I walked into the casita they used to share back then off State Road 14, known as the Turquoise Trail Scenic Byway, and they just handed me a joint as I entered. That started an immediate and lasting friendship.

I created a unique major in my studies at NYU combining psychology and art, which allowed me to find my calling very early in life to be a therapist specifically for creative professionals and the not-so-very-professional. Traditional therapy tends to clump people into categories of "normative" and "maladaptive" behavior, and normative is a category most artists have no interest in conforming to, and maladaptive can be somewhat of a resource for the art mind— even if it's a crippling blockade for others. Not to mention that traditional therapists want to pull their clients away from living in a world of fantasy, whereas it is specifically my job to instead nurture that very same impulse.

From the start, I understood how to motivate creative spirit in artists without boxing them into the triviality of pedestrian normalcy, which gives some an experience that feels like an idea of comfort. But our weird is our gift, our gateway, to the art life. I made a career out of that, rather than intermingle my own creative pursuits with the demands of commerce and industry. And I nurture my creativity any way it calls to me. I take photographs with black & white film as a practice of paying attention to what's around me and then cut out small fragments from old magazines to add an element of analog collage. I even make recorded music on occasion, playing with uncustomary harmonies finding unexpected overlap, into what are quirky short compositions of, I hope, a subtle charm. But I rarely even share those recordings. One of them I gave to a friend, and when attending a performance of modern dance, I sat in the audience thinking how these underground environments are exactly what I'd like to create for, and my song came on, just two seconds after I had that thought! My friend had invited me without even hinting she had used it for her piece, which I was so thrilled by. Alas, most people just think I'm a clothing designer, which I don't bother to deny. But I didn't buy into the allure of that success dynamic, the 'mattering' dynamic, the applause dynamic, which seemed vestiges of a capitalist influence on defining what is essential. I thought instead, "Isn't it, in the end, about creating a beautiful life?"

Good fortune really smiled on me to wind up in a town with so many well-off older creatives, with the resources and sensibility to appreciate counseling and self-reflection. It frees me to be someone that a person without access to insurance or even an extra $20, can talk to, off the clock. And you can't really be friends with paying clients, especially of more traditional therapy models that don't involve life coaching, so this lets me play a supportive role in my community that I feel good about, and even a valued participator.

Jacy is Native American, which is not uncommon here, because there are twelve different tribal pueblos within an hour of Santa Fe. That's more than half the Indian tribes overall in New Mexico. What you learn fairly quickly is that they are not "magical beings" from the recesses of white imagination, but real people with their hilarity, their sorrows, their sex appeal, their politics, their often-material aspirations alongside spiritual ones. And a few I know are really good bartenders, despite the myth of alcohol metabolism making them genetically poor drinkers. I will say, worth noting too from the art community I have experienced, Indians get well-versed in the history of modern and contemporary art, not just their own native traditions that go back hundreds of years, often faithfully maintained. Don't think you won't get a substantially informed conversation about Picasso, Dali, Basquiat, and Warhol when you bring up topics of art, or attend Santa Fe's Indian Market, the largest Native American art fair on the globe, bringing $160 million in revenue to the city each year. This is a community that fully understands and appreciates greatness, in both imagination and technique, transmitted onto canvas as well as to hide and feather.

Just as art is a primary unifier across cultures, so is the secret language of sweets. Jacy is carrying a whole bag of cotton candy grapes, which are not modified or infused as one immediately supposes after tasting them, but a lucky discovery of cross-pollinating wild grapes. So they're a natural accident and taste just like their sweet namesake. Like a moth to frothy light, I am enjoying them with him, though Jacy somewhat performs his ingestion of these wonders by throwing them up in the air and managing to have them land in his mouth with seemingly little effort and just the slightest tip back of the neck. What was I saying about not being magical?

"You got it Cybilline," he says encouraging me to eat with the same zestful technique. "I know you're down with brown," he says, "you got that duende." Duende being a Spanish notion for carrying a mysterious

29

indescribable 'it' quality that makes something enchanted and charming without being able to put your finger on exactly what makes it so. The Mona Lisa has duende, I suppose, because it sure isn't her beauty captivating all those people over the last 500 years. But something unidentifiable in her mystery magnetizes us to her.

Jacy's long straight black hair and sleeveless tee could be punk except he wears a cowboy hat, which is another thing that cowboy and Indian stories might have made you think was an uneasy pairing. But few in Santa Fe, unlike neighboring Texas, actually wear cowboy hats, and Jacy knows it's a statement piece, with its long flat brim. He blends cultures beautifully and at ease, and I adore him for it.

"Man, I am in such a teetering tizzy of late," he says. It's at this moment that Tina and Rolf break away from us, to greet a few canine friends further up in the brush. "I have this gallerist who was kind of demanding that I complete more work in order to keep me on, but I make the pieces I do because they come out of my life. It's how I breathe. I give you my sculpture, I'm giving you my blood. And he says that makes me an amateur; that a professional can make art every day like a job. Like making a pizza because there's an order for it on the phone. I was like, WHAT?!"

First thing to note is that Jacy's work is stunning and meticulous and of expert craftsmanship. The most recent pieces I saw included these fox-head men who lift their heads off their bodies. There is no gore or violence in it, it's just an awareness of persona, whose Latin root interestingly is "mask", and is also called so by Carl Jung in his model of the psyche. Not to mention the title of my favorite among the films by the great director, Ingmar Bergman. The only relation the decapitation has to death in his art, is the death of the illusion of the Self. The construct. The removing of the head is a move of power, to show mastery over identity. And the fox, a benevolence of spirit.

He may one day make them on call. But for now, those creatures are still building themselves in his psyche, each an individual that he must greet, respect, and learn from before producing its spirit's image into this world.

"That sounds like an amateur perspective by the gallerist," I propose.

"Being moved by inspiration is for hacks, were his words I believe," he says. "Did you look at my art and call me a hack?" "That's what you said?" I ask. "That's what I thought," he clarifies.

"Look, there are a lot of worldviews based on what we want from our lives. He's allowed to have his, he has a business to run," I tell him. "But it's important to identify that capitalism is just an economic system, and many make a religion of it, and usually it's people who would swear they don't buy into religion. But their entire sense of well-being and worth is based on what capitalism values; how much money they make, what job titles they achieve, what possessions they acquire. Basically finding truth in whatever begets financial success. And then all their opinions on value line-up under that godhead."

"Right, but what's good for the soul is often not good for the pocketbook. And he thinks I'm missing the truth with a capital T," he says in frustration. "Even using the word professional, to say you are valid and serious about what you do... it's so manipulative."

"Or it's manipulated," I say of the worldview.

Art is not like a restaurant where you serve up what you think the customer will want, which is not to be confused with entertainment. Unlike the latter, if you make something that other people think is terrible, then you have not failed. If the whole world disregards what you made, but it's beautiful to you, and fills you with appreciation for life, then you have succeeded wildly. It's if you change what you made to make them like it, but in the process no longer see the magic in it yourself; that is the betrayal. That is what Patti Smith refers to as "suck-cess" and why the hard pill to swallow for any creator is that it's part of the deal that people don't have to want to eat what you're serving. They are free to like gray and blue while you obsess over red. But then it's not their job to be you. And then sometimes they want it twenty years later, when you've moved on to making other dishes. All in love is fair.

So successful have corporate agendas been in our culture, that the concept of sell-out has been supplanted and lauded as just being savvy. But not everyone who creates wants "in" to the market. And the effect of the primacy of finance thinking, even in realms that relate to spirit, is that surface engagement and impulsiveness, neediness and grabbing, even deception, are all qualities that often get rewarded, as commerce motivating traits. But those all focus on external conquests, and not where success more often resides, in the internal realms.

"You don't need to be thrown off when people show you which game they're playing, right?" I shrug.

"OK, but it goes deeper," he says. Jacy stops walking and takes a look across the mountain range surrounding us. "Gosh, it's so beautiful," he says, mostly to himself. He makes a quick symbol with his hands, that had the feel of being reverential to our surroundings, but he may have had a cramp for all I know. It wasn't the kind of thing you interrupt to ask. "Umm... how do I say this," he continues, composing his thoughts. "Then I told this to Tina's mother and she said, 'I might even say it's a bit narcissistic to make only what is meaningful to yourself and expect to be paid for it.'" He turns to me and mock-grits his teeth to show his displeasure, and then spits out a terse-sounding last few lines, "when you have *responsibilities* to consider." Jacy puts his fingers to his temple. "So in 24 hours, I am charged with the narcissistic amateur label by people who I expect to support me." He smiles a big fake smile.

You have to dive very deeply into the self, to learn your true nature, your true desires, your own raison d'être so that you walk a path in alignment with your truth. Not the system's truth, or your mother's truth. That is why "Know thyself" is inscribed on the Temple of Apollo, a god of almost everything. To know yourself is how you can identify if you are growing or not, and in which direction to reach for next.

But listening to yourself is hard, which is why many listen to the demands of social obligation instead. What better excuse not to investigate the territories of the self than to pretend it is narcissism to do so. Some may even try to claim you must consider others at all times, to make your decisions only based on what others need. And think you selfish for not doing so, and never imagine how selfish it is of them to ask. How narcissistic to place the things they want from you above what your choices are. After all, someone desiring something from you doesn't mean you are obligated to give it. That's what the work of knowing yourself helps you decide.

I truly believe all art, while arguably self-absorbed and often pursued at the exclusion of all else, is ultimately a selfless altruistic practice to bring a unique sensibility and expression into the world. I believe it is a noble pursuit. And let's not forget, your light, by light's nature, also shines to and for others. But I pity the world had van Gogh adopted more socially correct behavior... something more productive and practical. Some might say, reasonable. That's not what we need him for. But most importantly, not what he needed from himself.

"It takes some time, and requires real care, to build your relationship to how you create, but it's actually a long-term investment," I suggest. "In both your happiness and the quality of what you do, to find your own way, in your own time." We take a few more steps in silence, before I blurt out, "I mean, if you're going to be a great artist or just any kind of spiritual person really, You BETTER get self involved!" His eyes light up.

And of course, this goes to the core of who we are. Your life is primarily a result of how you communicate with yourself... despite the attempt by so many to try to define themselves by what they perceive as the effects of circumstances they've experienced. But your relationship to your own energetics informs how you interpret —and then direct— your life. And the spin you put on whatever happens plays a big role in what happens next.

"What I'm learning is, you have to carry your protection close," he says, "which is kind of just hearing your own voice, sometimes, I think."

"Yeah, some might mistakenly tell you nurturing self love is narcissistic," I admit frankly, "but placing yourself above the foolish noise of the fray, is Excalibur."

He gasps. "I love that," Jacy says. His eyes are so charming when he smiles, it makes you like people. "Can I hug you?" he asks. "Sure," I shrug, and as he puts his arms around me, he whispers, "Excalibur. Wow."

I release from the hug and pinch his elbow. Partly because I think it's one of the most fun parts of the human body, possessing just that fleshy mound of skin and subcutaneous tissue, which contain no feeling, or alternatively the stinging jar of the funny bone. What a delicious part of our vessel; so very all or nothing.

"I know you know this," and I feel the enjoyment of my hair swaying from the slight tilt of my head, "but if, even when you're pressured from all sides, you can remember the Grail of Life is not something you obtain, not a physical thing— but something you trace to its roots energetically and become," and I pause to catch his glance, "then you'll never be chasing after the wrong prize."

He clasps his hands together in honor, and confides, "That's just it, I think I struggle at times to just Be, but Being should be easier than Doing," he says, and looks at the sky. "But doing creates ego, and dealing with your ideas of who you are, of self, make 'being' harder work than the doing, sometimes." He looks to meet my gaze and I join him in stillness. He holds up a cotton candy grape like a cheers, and I reach into the bag, and clink grapes with him. We both partake the sacrament.

"You know the old line, the truth shall set you free," I say, as we look at the incredible skyline of lenticular clouds, which look like UFOs, almost artificially constructed, and one suspects are hiding flying ships inside them. "As though there's some set truth," he mutters with a resigned laugh, looking back down at his sneakers.

"Well, it's using that great tool of Honesty that allows the Truth to set you free," I continue, "and it will always light the path forward."

It's funny but there's an old song that says honesty is such a lonely word, but I've been thinking about it, and that's really not the issue. It's that maturity is such a lonely word. And it's older people who often don't have it, so their confusions create even more blockades for young people who need their guidance most. And a cycle continues.

Tina and Rolf come running back and shift the dynamic of the moment. Rolf carries a stick almost twice as wide as his body is long, with a shifting look in his eyes that seems to say, "Continue with your wandering, I have found what's mine."

 RADIO REPORT: Car drives by the parking perimeter, with —The Go-Go's "Can't Stop The World"— blasting through the open windows.

"What's going on with you," I ask, "Everything good in Tina-land?"

"Oh yeah," she says, "I'm working on a decay series." She grabs the stick from Rolf and impressively throws it far enough for him to have to leap. "I should use this stick actually," she realizes, "as Rolf dissolves it."

"I'm intrigued," I say, smiling. She nods and explains, "It's just that I've been seeing how much of life and nature is about decay," she says. "Daily beauty maintenance, you wash your face to remove dead skin. You brush your teeth twice a day, and while we don't necessarily have to shave our legs every single day, men definitely have to shave their face every fucking morning."

"I don't," Jacy insists, "but even so, OK, yeah its weekly."

"I just mean there's an endless onslaught of upkeep," she says. "The facial hair is new life yet it's kind of like dust building up every day on your face."

"You know," I suddenly realize, "that's the same with weeds. They are new growth but they're also decay building up in your yard."

"Yes!" she shrieks. "It's about how everything needs to be regularly cleaned up, refreshed. But right now, I'm focusing on the physical body as kind of a part one of the series."

"So how do you visually tell that story?" I say in appreciation. I was drawn to art by the facts of aesthetics, but also because I was always charmed by artistic minds and the creative solving of riddles.

"Well actually, it started with a cougar tooth, because Jacy's aunt has access to all these wild animal teeth from the jewelry she makes, and the cougar tooth was really an unusual find. You need your teeth so bad in the wild to survive, it's a dirty trick for nature to rob you of such a thing. But that's decay. And then his aunt was putting these arch supports in her shoes, and so I thought of the arch of your foot, which exists to support the weight of your body so that you can walk and run. Such basic function! But elasticity declines, and then you need arch supports!"

"Decay," I repeat, mulling it over. She hands Jacy the leash to unburden herself from Rolf. I see her will to push back on his physical demands is also decaying right before our eyes.

"Well the trick is I'm trying to present it from a positive," she says, at age 23. "So I've made casts of the cougar tooth, and my own high arch, and I'm inlaying gold leaf up the arch and the side of the tooth, and collecting facial hair remains from my brother's electric razor, as dust, to sprinkle on the gum side of adhesive paper. And it's gonna be real simple so it feels like a meditation on decay and not any dark heavy gloom piece."

"And for the opening, she's going to perform a dance on these themes," Jacy says, with a barely concealed tone of gushing. It can be so trying handing out praise to our partners. "Yeah," she nods, "I'm carefully constructing a ripped gown to move in."

"Oh I thought he was joking," I gasp, "that's amazing." I can't help but let out a laugh at that playful articulation, appreciating the indulging of every path to making a commentary, and I rest my hand on her shoulder. I took modern dance for a few years in New York, and I have to say, if you could reduce life to averages, dancers are the most lovely people in the world. Not just because the language they speak is grace, but unlike all other art forms, where you have a physical object left as evidence of your toil, dancers specialize in ephemera, undertaken with a purity where the reward is only in the experience of doing. They work painstakingly for months, on every detail of a mode of speaking that few even have the tools of articulation to deeply comprehend, and once it's performed one or two nights, there is no record of it. Nothing to show for it, or return to ten years later and re-live as one of the cornerstones of your experience. It is created for the moment only and released. Much like a firefly. Which tends to result in dance attracting practitioners to it that are unusually capable at enacting the uncommon trait of selflessness.

And what does endure is that even if someone spends just a couple years as a dancer, infusing that relationship to elegance into your body is like adding a few extra colors of nuance to your emotional palate that you dip into for the rest of your life. Even though in many ways it's an artform of letting go.

"I'm trying to create acceptance for decay as inevitable process," she clarifies, "and kind of acknowledging the opportunity to be given the tools to run, to chew, in the first place." "I love this girl," Jacy says, pulling her close.

"It's pretty sweet," I concur. "And so positive, bravo." And that's not surprising. Like dance, Santa Fe attracts people of a certain sensibility, a magical lightness of being. I compare the college kids drawn to Santa Fe University of Art & Design to others, and can't help but note that they tend to have an ingrained spirituality paired with an earnest innocence. It's a surprisingly common trait here that is uncommon throughout the modern world generally. And they're skilled. Some of these students play in three separate bands and play different instruments in each one, and do it well. With feeling and aplomb, not mechanically.

"What's especially intriguing to me about this project is that young people tend to be freaked out by decay and waste," I mention, "because it usually takes a bit of living to see that nature's perceived atrocities tend to have their reasons."

"It's like how people are freaked out by the gore of the body," Jacy relates, "and death. Then you meet a doctor and they're entirely unflustered and without any horror. They see it all every day, it's commonplace and normal. But meanwhile people are traumatized. I think native culture in general is much more comfortable with mortality."

"Than most of America, yes," Tina points out, "but New Mexico of course is calavera central. Skulls are part of the everyday aesthetic, from Day of the Dead to low rider interiors... but we're the exception to many rules."

"Maybe it's that Pueblo people have a greater focus on transitioning to the spirit world as something more to be celebrated than mourned?" he questions. "I don't know..."

"A knowledge that lives recycle..." I offer. It's funny, there are so many people who think that belief in an afterlife is the result of being afraid of death and not being able to cope with the finality of it. That it's the easy way out for those of delicate sensibility. Of course, the opposite is true. If all you do is drop in the soil, you are off the hook. The much more daring —and for some, terrifying— belief is that you can't escape your choices, can't escape your evolutionary demands. You remain accountable. And yes, you'll still have to get another tedious job. "Hmmm..." I start to ruminate. "In a way, the whole job market could be characterized as living off decay."

"What?" Jacy laughs. I laugh too but it's true.

"I'm just saying it could be argued that all the billions of meaningless jobs people have, where even the company's end goal is ultimately just more surface noise in the culture, or manipulatively destructive to our psyches, or damaging to our environment. In the end, all that effort put into making things happen, and the enormous pressures felt to get things done, doesn't accomplish much discernible good or beauty as an end result, but just furthering a cycle of materiality and false hype, where the effect is not much more than a mouse running on a wheel. It can seem daunting and depressing."

"Yeah that did sound very depressing," Tina confirms. Jacy laughs again. "Myth of Sisyphus and Death of a Salesman, wrapped in one," he says.

"But to your point," he continues, "her project got me thinking about the waste concept just in how nature is set up. When a guy comes, he releases up to a billion sperm cells in one go, just to try 'n fertilize one egg. Which it usually doesn't succeed at. Talk about a waste-based process!" Rolf halts our march forward, as he sniffs the ground, intent on making the most of his opportunity to besmirch the land. "That said," I say watching Rolf paw the dirt, "the result of all that massive waste is us. So who are we to question how the game is structured."

It's a weird thought I suppose, but when considering the sustainability of modernity, just walk into any airport bathroom— with the lines, the endless chorus of flushing from that consumerist desperation of our digestive systems, and just listen to the constant explosive gurgle of expulsion. It always speaks to me like doom. In one moment, experiencing the rush of bodies walking in and out, the loud flush flush flush of all the foods everyone has been ingesting, the paper cups and cardboard boxes that carried those foods, the gasoline for cars and planes that brought those travelers who flush flush flush in a metronome of human journeying.

If that much processing of seemingly endless waste is on display in each moment of every airport bathroom in every city of each state of every developed nation, then you know, our time here is limited, and we better enjoy the window of activity we have, for it is not endless. We too will go down the toilet— Our time will come, as we are not the last race of Being that will inherit this Earth, just as the dinosaurs occupied this same land for 165 million years before us. The Earth has more plans for life after we're done.

"Maybe my point is an odd one..." she wonders. "That all of that, whether it's the presence of decay or the seeming pointlessness of culture, the going around in circles, is all okay. That it's how it's always been."

I actually have always thought Warhol got that more than any other artist in history. That it was a rare bird that really took the lead and endeavored the way forward, and that —just like the top point of a pyramid— all else followed behind that odd destiny paver. And instead of feeling a morose disappointment in humanity's lack of verve, that those leader-follower ratios could be enjoyed. That it could even be funny, all the lack of motivation and capacity that dwells in this creature of foible. When you see humans like other animals, that run and eat and play, it all just makes more sense. Because it's how the human race got here, after all. And who could deny our main motivations are still the same as any animal; a battle for territory, access to food, and a vying for sex partners. But despite all our perceived failings, we still produced Jimi Hendrix. We still produced Maya Deren. We produced Bruce Lee. We produced Nikola Tesla, Mahatma Gandhi, you name it. And that 'the remainders' are not examples of falling short; but that we could still turn the camera on anyone in the crowd, and if placed in the right conditions, make a movie around them. That very few had to be leaders but that all had their role.

"The way it's always been, is right..." Jacy says, shrugging. "That's the Medicine Wheel. The circle of life and its four directions, the circle of time and its four seasons." He hands us each a grape.

I playfully hold up the grape toward the sun, the source it came from, and let the light shine through its flesh.

Jacy leans against my shoulder and rocks back again. Throws another grape into the air and down the hatchet.

I leave the dog park thinking about how gone are the days of the Wise Elders living up on the hill, and that modernity offers some interesting challenges in finding a way back to the intergenerational dialogue that is so needed. It used to be that music could bring grandchild to grandparent together, with songs commonly ingested by radio. The artful unification by way of a favorite song, humanity united by the threads of melodic intermingling. Now more often than not, everything is listened to in the private world of headphones, from the private playlist, and not the open space of shared living rooms. And it's often parents that youth cannot go to, cannot rely on, cannot believe in. Cannot be healed by.

While it's easier than ever to video chat across long distances, and create family gatherings from different cities, these same technologies and modalities have concurrently caused greater distances between us interpersonally. The space of things unsaid increases with the distance of a plastic screen and only one person speaking at a time. The name of the game is isolation, even amid all that connectivity.

Ironically, there was a time when people would say, "If we only knew what each other was thinking and weren't so isolated, we'd have peace on Earth." Now that we're all intertwined and know too much about what everyone is thinking, we're horrified, over-stimulated, and increasingly uneasy about human connectivity. So if society at times looks like it's fraying at the seams, that might be so.

People also used to worry that television was brainwashing a generation, but things have complicated exponentially. Networks, owned by international conglomerates, still control what messages are placed into programming. Advertising still shows off particular comforts to be indulged and fetishized. But while the general public predominantly controls what they're exposed to on the internet through their own social media feeds, which is a form of personalized magazine, a strange thing happens: While the editor has left the building, ideology is now shared with no checks and balances of true logical rigor, to ensure validity of content and truth in messaging, beyond what 'sounds good' or 'feels good' which in turn creates a vacuum where the internet can do more brainwashing than television ever could. Often the people creating these dynamics of thought manipulation aren't even aware they're doing it. It's an age of accidental propaganda.

If you ever get a chance to look at political posters from the Cuban Revolution of the 1960s and 70s, you'll notice one thing very immediately: Mind control used to be so much more artful.

SEQUENCE FOUR

 RADIO REPORT: — "I WANT TO SEE THE BRIGHT LIGHTS TONIGHT" BY LINDA AND RICHARD THOMPSON— PLAYS.

It was one of those nights. I wanted to keep the hum of electricity usually present in any contemporary home as low wattage as possible. I unplugged all the electronics from the wall, and allowed only candles for light, keeping the windows only partially open to silence the breezes that seemed to be picking up, and not disturb the flames on the wicks. The heat on my fingers from each strike of the matchbook, part of an activation.

I put on my sheer nightgown early, to feel unencumbered; even candlelight is enough to visually pierce through the material. And in the silence of the night, I see terrific expressions of lightning across the sky, but no thunder at all. Walking out onto the deck, I could feel the electricity in the air. The little hairs on the arm become alert, the shivers of goosebumps through the nervous system, while looking up at dynamic strikes in all directions across the sky. Wind streams and Zeus' bolts of light, but no rainwater and no sounds.

The environmental miraculism of such a unique atmospheric climate is part of the same energetics that pull artists to this region. It's about a sense of magic in the air, ever present, but occasionally more dramatic and visually undisguised. The veil pulled back. Another lightning strike. I imagine trying to catch it on film, and I pick up my phone. Then put it down and grab my camera. Take a deep breath and put that back down too. A photo is not where I want to document this; I want it documented in my senses.

Blowing out the candles, I choose only to listen to the magnetic silence and watch the sky.

Once the lightning had dissipated, there was still a charged yet tranquil feeling to the evening. I grabbed the car keys, and just held them in my hands for a few moments. I didn't want to disturb the peace with actions, but needed to invite in more emergent energy, more of the night. I remained in my nightgown and walked barefoot to the car. I hesitated before starting the engine, but even Esmerelda seemed to be game. Let's ride, she purrs.

There's an ancient pagan belief in the relationship of the barefoot and the unconscious. Why ceremonies are performed dancing with bare feet is that the sole of the foot touching the soil of the earth is considered a direct conduit to the unseen inner world; the hidden unconscious of the mind meeting that which is buried and hidden deep in the land. The Earth itself, an outer skin, helping us tap into our innermost dream realms.

My naked foot and the car's brake system is a less primal coalescence, but I drive slowly but dreamlike, guided, toward the nearby St. John's campus field. As is customary, I've left the seatbelt unbuckled to avoid constraint.

It is summer and in between sessions, and late— so the road is free of traffic as I turn into the campus entrance. Driving away from the tall streetlights, down a winding road, I hesitate to follow my instinct to turn the headlights off, but then shut down my own resistance. As despite the dark of night, the quality of the moon's glow is shine enough to see the road. The lot was empty and Esmerelda pulls her frame into a spot facing the field. The night air was palpable through the car windows and I was content to look at the stars shining past the parting clouds, with their radiance framed by the curve of the windshield.

But like the siren call, I felt I could tempt fate: toes to grass and in flowing sheer nightgown, I walked further into the field. Looking up and in utter peace, silently— three lights in pyramidic shape took form above me. I clasp my own hand. They began to slightly lower, slowly, and like the lightning earlier, are accompanied by no sound. I tilt my head gently, with only appreciative intrigue and wonder. The lights change in hue to pink. My nostrils flare, registering the scent of the desert mist activating the lavender and Russian sage.

I continue making strict eye contact with the hovering structures, not wanting to move or flee, but to observe and perhaps offer. Like encountering an animal in the wild, remaining still as to not frighten or chase away a venerated entity or presence. And suddenly, the startling sound of a deer bolting from position, back toward the surrounding Sangre de Cristo mountains, called my attention toward the trees. I put my hand to my chest to catch myself, with a gasp, and quickly looked back up. In just that singular instant, the three lights had vanished. I squint through the misty evening air.

It starts to rain lightly, finally piercing that space between the expectant and the actualized. I relent and get back in the car, quickly rolling up the windows, peering up again to search the skies. Car lights on, Esmerelda and I look for movement. The rain on the windshield, instead of following gravity and splashing downward off the car, act in counter motion. The droplets drag upward on the windshield, as if they too are looking skyward, gravity be damned.

  RADIO REPORT: DRIVING BACK, RADIO IS ON AND —SUFJAN STEVENS "CONCERNING THE UFO SIGHTING"— PLAYS IN A HUSH ACROSS A SILENT CITY.

SEQUENCE FIVE

On summer Fridays in Santa Fe, there's always a contagious vibe of gallery hopping. The city comes alive with free events and openings, and the Railyard, Siler auto-district, and area surrounding the Historic Plaza, have the art and music shows that modern and contemporary art paramours instinctively go for. There is further charm available up on Canyon Road, which has a varied mix of sophisticated, well-crafted, more traditional work on display, often with wine in hand. But as impressive a statement as is made about a city's commitment to culture by having a mile-long street dedicated solely to the existence of art right in the heart of downtown, it's true that Canyon also has the distinction of an admittedly uneasy amalgamation of creations, sometimes leaning toward that unfortunate category of art that aspires to the Walmart poster section. But whatever your fancy, a sense of creative festivity tends to pervade all over town.

It's at these local culture hubs that the age barriers really dissolve, and people are brought together by something much deeper and more substantial than what year they were born. United by a love of invention and play, Santa Feans eyeball, ogle, and drink in this wide variety of creations, and they speak to whoever is next to them in appreciation of the work, and sometimes just the spirit of endeavoring. People don't really go to bars to find a date here, they go to galleries and the Friday night Art Walk.

"Hey, I've seen you just about everywhere, it feels like," a spirited woman says, with ringlet hair worn much like a garland, framing eyes that have the atmosphere of daring I tend to encourage. And there's a guy dancing in contained but aware movements next to her, almost drawing attention to the fact that the music on, while not so loud, and easily overlooked, is worth the ear's attention. He has a concho leather belt with fringe tassels that hangs down the upper side of his leg, which draws some attention to his swaying and compelling male features. I really do like a man who's in touch with his hips.

RADIO REPORT: — "VIDEO LIFE" BY CHRIS SPEDDING— IS HEARD PLAYING OVER THE GALLERY SPEAKERS.

I reach out my hand to her in a cordial greeting, and as I do this, Ting-Ting, who runs a store in town with all local artist-made clothing, grabs my other wrist. I laugh and we quickly hug. "Sorry, this is my friend Ting-Ting, and you are?" "Gwendolyn!" She almost jumps up on her toes when she says that. She's probably in her late 20s, which is this age where people often worry they are getting older because they're not 22 anymore, and imagine 30 as a mark in the sand, indicating the end of dreaming, the long storied great party of life coming to a close. Which just makes me laugh and laugh and laugh and laugh... "Oh and this is my friend Angus," she says, pulling him physically into our little circle, and out of whatever world he was languidly dreaming in a moment ago. He does snap right to attention.

This long-haired creature is a specimen. Playful, probably irresponsible, definitely at least into his mid 30s, but ...between his style, his movements, and that hanging leather belt, I'm seeing a man exuding creativity, a total lack of machismo, secure in his skin. But when his hand grips mine, it's a warm solid masculine energy. And as we lean towards each other, he looks at my earring. After barely a pause, he says "That's really great." And I'm looking at the curve of his mouth and thinking, how many men even notice an earring? That's what's great. I catch his outstretched arm and can see the pulse of his veins.

The show at the gallery is also all about pulse, and the uniqueness of being; or more specifically, the anatomical intrigue of our own fingerprints. A room-size installation by artist Rafael Lozano-Hemmer, that measures each visitor's pulse while registering your own thumbprint on the screen, which joins a whole wall-length display of these beating pulses and finger lines, from the fellow guests. Each visitor's distinct thumb impression then rhythmically flashes in sync with heart rate, creating a throbbing visual mass of humanity in an intense, personal, poetic way, joined together by the recurring lines of symmetry found in our cellular biology.

Then there's a piece in the corner with its own headphones, called "The Pulse Armed With a Pen" by artist Dario Robleto, that's equally as poetic and personal. It contains a sound recording that was pressed onto twin golden records and encased in aluminum, which was sent into space, comprised of the compressed brainwaves and heartbeat of someone in the energetic throes of falling in love. To think NASA with all its bureaucracy and square governmental influence, could be coaxed into performing an act so poetic, and sending that into the uncharted cosmos, is astonishing. It reminds us all to dream that anything is possible, because nothing is so set that it can't be potentially inched quietly towards an exotic articulation.

The challenge posed by the artist in the text displayed next to the recording: "What if an advanced alien technology could take the audible recordings of the electrical signatures of her heart and mind, and decipher the meaning." Taking in the conceptualization of this work made me think humanity really does sometimes transcend itself.

When you experience art at this striking level in a small desert town, it only magnifies the effect, mixing big city access with the big sky beauty, and yet intimacy of scale, that we experience it in.

Further on display tonight in the Railyard are performances in association with the Currents New Media Art + Technology Festival, an annual show of digital interactive immersive work, which includes outdoor performances that project motion-correlative images on large screens behind an electronic band in outlandish dayglo attire. We dance for a while in the early evening air, where people in their seventies are as likely to startle with their dance bravado and style as someone in their twenties. There are in fact free music shows, and sometimes movies, in the Railyard throughout the summer weekends, not to mention free music in the Plaza bandshell every weekday from mid-June to mid-August.

But as we dance, Ting-Ting and I are shouting to each other over the music in a bit of a giddy state, already making plans to meet up for the early shift of the International Folk Art Market, coming up in just two more weeks. The biggest festival of its kind in the world, over 150 master folk artists from 50 countries all fly to the City Different for a weekend market of unique artifacts. One-of-a-kind blankets, paintings, jewelry, textiles, accessories, highly detailed knives, handwoven carpets, belts, bags— literally every expression of creative industriousness undertaken by the human hand. A sea of people, with 20,000 attendees flocking to the high desert and descending on Museum Hill to FIND THAT THING they didn't know existed, but have just gotta get. I bring cash to limit me, because otherwise I will go overboard in the wrong form of excess. But really, it's like the whole world is gathering for a massive culture party in Santa Fe every year.

Many hungers do catch up with one while arting the night away, so Gwendolyn uses her ability to segue moments, to help the four of us regroup and readily embark together on what is commonly known as #HowToSantaFe. Quickly grabbing a reservation for tapas at La Boca, we still have a half hour to kill, and start with a round of mixologist cocktails at Santa Fe Spirits, the tasting room bar of our local distillery, with all alcohol made purely of Southwestern botanicals. We then zip up the street to have bacon wrapped dates, manchego and quince, bruschetta, and sliced flat iron steak with a sea salt caramel sauce for dinner at La Boca. Then catch an on-the-fly reservation at Joseph's Culinary Pub for dessert, where three of us devour their silky Butterscotch Pudding, an experience in texture and flavor that is cause for alarm, which I can only liken to a faerie form of crack. Angus gets the towering meringue Cloud Cake with tarragon-grapefruit, and I take particular note of the abandon he eats it with. Such a lack of restraint in the right context generally suggests good times.

The waitress speaks to us in hushed tones; almost conspiratorial. She knows I sometimes begin with dessert in place of a salad, and in making a special trip just for this one prized portion of a meal, we are demanding greatness from our evening. It's the Santa Fe way. Her joy in our enthusiasm becomes part of our experience, but we are not done infusing magic just yet. There is more debauch awaiting, as we head over to Santacafe, our fourth culinary stop of the night, to close with the Midas Touch cocktail. This delectable mystery has 18 ingredients and is one of the more unique sensorial experiences of this world. It leaves you transported, and spoiled rotten, with a gold speckled essence that lingers at the bottom of the glass. You swirl with your wrist and behold, replaying what you've tasted, watching the sunset of the drink, before the night turns black.

I never tire of the inherent ambiance of uplift from restaurant dining, because somehow I've never lost sight of the extraordinary honor it is for our species to access the uncustomary regality of being served at leisure, picking delicacies from a menu of options, being prepared by someone passionate about unearthing the potential suavity of every flavor. Instead of rabidly chasing animals on foot in the dark and pouncing on scattering prey with our bare teeth. And the thought of whatever that might taste like.

When I finally glance down at my watch, I see 10:22 staring back at me. Even on a Friday, 9 pm is still "Santa Fe midnight"... You can feel the city pulling up the sheets and rolling into bed. This is another part of the small-town aspect of this international city. The culture is not built around nightlife, but instead around the demands for a high quality of daylife.

Cybilline is an extraordinarily beautiful woman, Angus thinks. They don't make them that pretty anymore; an unavailable biology, sent off to more advanced alien worlds to exist in higher realms than this. She is so unapologetic about her beauty and fearless in her expression. She knows she is making waves. Just walking into the room, she seems to state, 'the normal set of standards is unacceptable and I will transcend it' but she does it without any threat or intimidation. She does it in delight. She makes it fun. It's a sense of pleasure most of us wish we could give ourselves permission to have.

She challenges, and even crashes, the status quo, but doesn't make others feel inadequate in that, or disrespected. We feel encouraged by her to explore a deeper self. To stop playing footsie with the shoreline, and jump into the sea. She's not telling you who to be, but to go find out.

But people rarely respect themselves enough to be totally who they really are, and therein lies the inability to extend that respect to others. We approve of them when they get in alignment with what we think and want. But where is the generosity of letting others explore their possibilities, wherever that process takes them, just as we demand that freedom, that authority, ourselves.

"Cybilline," he calls out after the group has all disbanded, and comes dashing over to that aqua blue vehicle containing the golden-haired woman Angus Hannigan has a new fascination with. "Hey..." he says, now fingering along my open window, "that was an amazing night. Just want to thank you for being our guide." He shifts his body weight in a way that lithely inhabits every muscle, and he never fills the conversational space with unneeded vowels. He opens his mouth and nothing spills out, as he ponders what to say, but you receive the communication that he is wanting to speak and there's no rush. He is at home in silence.

"There's a film playing at CCA on Tuesday night, I am pretty sure you would dig it. Actually, it's called *Cavedigger*."

CCA is the Center for Contemporary Art, which has its own cinematique, one of the three arthouse cinemas in the city, which matches the total aggregate of commercial movie theaters available here. I haven't heard about this film yet, but confess "Well honestly, I've never seen a bad film at CCA. They really curate what they show, it's something I love about this town. Of course I'll go." I smile but use my eyes more to show that I appreciate the gesture. I've always believed that nonverbal communication is best left away from the mouth. "Great, 7:15." He taps the top of the window twice, and off he goes, with just one quick glance back as he climbs into his black jeep.

  RADIO REPORT: — "Loving is Easy" by Rex Orange County with Benny Sings— plays on the car radio on the drive home.

The usual evening routine follows: wash the face, floss the teeth, apply a dash of Protein Serum and Olay Total Effects Fragrance Face Moisturizer. Then right into the open jar I go, becoming tonight, what is now 74 fireflies. The netted top is sealed for the night by that same strange hand. Clouds seem to float inside the room.

SEQUENCE SIX

I turn the brass hot water spigot and wait for the temperature to rise. The shower wall has many adobe nichos with mosaic tile backsplashes, on which are stashed an array of small decorative colored plastic bottles and vials, with genie tops. Encased within, a fine selection of fragranced moisturizers and essential skin oils, some filled only with dreams and night stories; empty bottles of imaginary potions.

Peach fuzz... soft light invisible hairs on supple surfaces. Squeeze lightly to extract juice.

The ritual of preparing for a new day, with all its possibilities, starts here. The steam opens your pores and softens the flesh, just right and tender. Every region a person may place their fingers, their nose, their mouth, must be a new oasis of scent and softness, like climbing a mountain in the dead of night, and feeling your way across dewy crevices and textures, stumbling upon each territory with the exaltation of surprise.

I lather and caress. My wet hair kisses my neck. Flavors of jasmine, coconut, lavender, mango... each find a spot for world explorers to languidly come upon, in their journey, where I am the earth surface, and they, the fingers that reach, prod, and search.

Each note of light fragrances penetrates the senses, as innocently entrancing as a 26-year-old Joni Mitchell playing a dulcimer to enraptured audiences of the BBC. The bee enters the flower and gathers the nectar for future honey. I twist another bottle top.

Angels meet you in these private moments that no one else sees or knows of, the invisible caves of consciousness, that others think are just nothing. No Lightened Being is mistaken on such topics, however— the timbre of your destinies are made in those private gardens, not just life's outward battlefields and sanctuaries, or the hallways of business pavilions, where is found the conducting of so much professional intercourse.

Unlike lungs, the skin breathes under the water, and I let out a sigh that could be misconstrued by listening ears. A hummingbird comes to the window to peek inside, for sweet water is what he seeks. Those tiny winged beasts can stick their tongues out for the elixir an incredible 17 times a second. The little heathens. My neck eases back in a circular motion to ingest the heat, and transform its insistent pounding into oxygen flow.

Turning off the shower, I leave my eyes closed. I listen to the universe, where there is a balance you can tap into, the way a satellite stays spinning by moving in the same direction and speed as the Earth itself. It's a track you align with, an opening to a frequency, a sense of harmony. No, there's nothing to hear. But there is a poetry of energy. You can listen to it the way you swing in a hammock and are gently rocked by it.

Slowly rubbing moisture along the back ligament behind the knee, and a different ointment just above the navel. Where else might a wandering pair of lips find itself? A different fragrance there. These salves are like a cookie shop, where you can take just one bite of each morsel in its most luscious creamy spot, and simply leave the rest, as a pure indulgent display of bounty and the lavish glories known only among the plentiful. These I make with an assortment of essential oils mixed in cocoa butter, to infuse scent as well as moisture in my scientifically formulated potions of ever-renewal.

I take, by instinct, a clash of color and pattern from the closet, that match only due to my love for them, each piece with hand sewn snippets and fibers affixed playfully to adorn. The car keys for Esmerelda are kept on a hook in the kitchen. That heavy turquoise door has become a symbol for adventure to me.

Cybilline has a scent, which she discovered at the earth age of 20. She was living in New York City then, and sniffed all around the street fairs, new age shops, and even the necks of her fellow city dwellers, in search of (and knowing it existed) a fragrance that was to be her signature emblem. That thing that would linger and say "Cybilline has been here— Track her, if you dare, but especially if you must!" She's worn it every day, for almost 40 years since. And if you're one to think 20 is too young to ever truly know some-thing everlasting, then take this identity fragrance parable to recognize, and maybe even appreciate, your folly. Knowing is not about the age printed on your driver's license.

She jiggles an intrusion into my orifice, turning it to an unlocked and open position, and the blood rushes through my veins to the engine, which revs and burbles. She puts her foot down on me with care. She senses my moods, and she delights in me always. We both share a dislike of the cold, and when I fail to start on first or second try in those times, she says, "I know exactly how you feel." She is my ultimate driver.

My stereo is always on it seems with the songs that match what's happening in my driver's mind and heart, my dear Cybilline; I know because she sings. The tunes always seem to be drawn in through my antenna and channeled out through the speakers. Her voice melodious, her finger taps like a heartbeat.

She takes hold of the steering wheel. She has gained back control. I am no longer able to narrate. The loquaciousness of the engine relents.

I look directly into the speedometer that I've always taken to be Esmeralda's inner eye. Then note my painted pink nail polish against the blue steering wheel; together hand and circle speak in color code grace. Combined, such a sturdy alliance.

Turning left down Don Diego Avenue, I take a quick detour toward the French breakfast spot, Clafoutis, to grab some soft fried beignets with powdered sugar, a treat made there only on Saturday mornings. I then barrel toward I-25 on my way to the kooky artist town of Madrid, located just 25 minutes outside of city limits. It was on this very drive that the original thought occurred to me to solidify moving to Santa Fe... surrounded by all that beauty and peace and unique majesty of the desert landscape in my initial days here, the quiet whisper of purpose arose. I recall realizing the question was not "Could I live here" but "Do I DESERVE to live here?" And with that enthusiastic affirmation of *Yes*, essentially graduated to making a home in the Land of Enchantment, and now I can't imagine considering an alternative. Everything else pales.

Just think, before automobiles, you couldn't just pick up and transport yourself to the social network or environment of your highest desires. You were stuck in whatever milieu you were born into, with whatever prejudices, preferences, and predilections governed that area. All those disconnected small towns, their own set of social rules, churches, diners. It's been 5,000 long years since we invented the wheel, alongside increasing our travel options to donkey, horse, and saddle, but still confined in speed and distance to the hungers and aches of our fellow mammals. Then finally, 200 years ago, the locomotive joined the relocation game. But it's only been a little more than a hundred years that we've added the outrageous adaptability provided by the car engine in mass production. If you're ever feeling impatient about anything, think about that really long wait to just be able to hit the open road! Make no mistake, the automobile was a godsend to our development and a phenomenal multiplier of our entire palette of life choices. We are forever in its debt, and to the wiles of Henry Ford for the cunning tactic of his manly and hyper-efficient assembly line.

A roadrunner darts across the road and I giggle involuntarily. It makes perfect sense that this is the state bird of New Mexico. It has a truly bizarre gate when it runs, that jerks back and forth, and gives no clear indication of why it should produce such a burst of speed, being almost as fast as a galloping horse.

The gods had a huge sense of humor the day they came up with this creature. And its little colored hairs that wiggle atop its head only add to their goofy character. But they are so fast, strong and finely tuned, that they can outgun rattlesnakes in the sudden strike department, and are regularly the victor in those confrontations with its desert-born neighbor. Perfect for the New Mexican ideal, part of the cuckoo family, and not just an eccentric outsider, but a solitary, lone adventurer.

RADIO REPORT: — "Afraid" by Nico— plays as road breezes kick up in a tussle and shimmy the hair.

That's also a good description of the characters that inhabit the most proudly oddball area of Santa Fe County, out in Madrid, New Mexico.

Once a town of gunslingers and outlaws, it enjoyed a short boom as a thriving mining town, but after Pearl Harbor, the demand for coal disappeared and it went from 2,000 people to becoming a ghost town like so many settlements whose resources fell out of commercial favor, and rebirthed itself into a hippy art colony, decades later. Like a Warhol superstar, it changed its name from MadRID (like the Spanish city) to MADrid, to emphasize the mad artist persona of its particular brand of rubble-rousers, inhabiting these makeshift dwellings but also mad to live, mad to dream. Now a place with just 300 residents, 290 of which are self-identified artists, writers, and musicians, and 280 of which are actually pretty darn good. Sometimes it may tend toward the thrift store painting, and the used, abused, and in any case repurposed. But the kind of thrift store you'd like to live inside for a good year or two in mind-altering bohemian bliss, if not for the sulfur-infused and correspondingly odorous water that spews out of local pipes.

They affectionately call themselves "Madroids."

I tell you, first time I set foot in the place, I walked by a young man strumming a guitar with no strings, and after a quick double take, I just nodded my head, "I like these people." They have an annual freak flag parade and a 'He/She Bang' gender-bending performance night, often featuring big tough traditionally male-identified men donning dresses and garters without shaving any body hair or bothering to effect gentility, which comes across somehow with more hilarity than the more ambiguous cross-dressing stylists. And of course there's the Christmas Lights display, with very intentionally mis-matching lights, sprawled from building to building. It expresses the diverse and accepting character of a community founded on weird. From my first drive out there, I made friends who I still count among my favorite people, and there's a whole tribe of them that feel like we've been having conversations for 30 years now, even if it's been just five.

"What do you think of this," Elsye asked, holding up a glittery fabric intersected with red and purple felting, no doubt made by her own hand.

She draped it around her shoulders, and only then did you realize she already had the same glitter color in her eye make-up, and a touch of red dye in her hair that accentuated the felting. Seeing the recognition in my eyes, she laughs, and lifts the fabric as a backdrop to her beauty instead of her accoutrement.

"Oh god I hope it doesn't read as glib and shallow," she says with a giggle. "Too much?" "What artist ever mistook aesthetics for shallow?" I reply with an eyebrow raised and a light-hearted smirk.

She points at me. "Higher life form," she proclaims. "Why don't people know that, Cybilline?" "What, that aesthetic comprehension is an indicator of perceptual depth?" She nods. "Cause they're dull as a stick," I explain with clear insight. When Elsye laughed, she let you feel the joy from her tone. "You got it Sister," and tapped my arm three times.

It is a curious Earth conundrum. In a vain attempt to not be fooled by appearances, which people are radically fooled by anyway, there's a huge subset of the population that askew paying attention to their looks, their clothes, their home decor, in some misguided belief that there is advancement in their aesthetic starvation. That the sheer plainness and passionlessness of their presentation connotes a depth of awareness, that they are no-nonsense, when in fact it connotes nothing but a lack of style.

Let me tell you something of the cosmos. Evolution loves details. Far beyond the triviality of human ego and its minor power plays, there exists a staggering paintbrush that gives the peacock its royal plumage, the mandarinfish its Kandinsky color glow, and the thousand strokes of golden follicle on the polygamous lion and its kingly mane. There is nothing understated and proper about a sunset, a field of wild weeds in bloom, or the astounding feathers of the secretary bird of the Sahara, which in some ways is Africa's version of the roadrunner. With quill-like feathers at the back of its head, the long gray feathers resembling a tailcoat, and dark feathers that look like britches, you have an artist's rendition of an old-fashioned secretary, who is quite the crazy old bird. But never drab!

If you think a walk through a hiking path takes your breath away, with its typically mono-colored green trees and brown earth and blue sky, just prepare yourself for the sights of space. With explosive supernovae and the floating webbed emissions from hot gas like airborne paint across a canvas of stars, intersecting a wash of spewing bubbles blown by radiation. And absolutely, there are similar hints of an expression of this impulse toward true cosmic beautificness here on the third rock from our star, like volcanic lighting, the aurora borealis, and the prismatic geothermal pools and formations you can experience in places like Yellowstone National Park.

But point being, it's not a universe that pretends to not care about art and aesthetics. It's integral to function.

"Let's just run in here for a second," she says going into one of the local galleries, filled with quirkily offbeat artful concoctions. It's not that everything is so well made, it's more the charm of the idea of who would think to make it in the first place.

I wait outside. I like the person who runs the shop a lot, but the sun on the skin in Madrid, which is 1,000 feet lower elevation than over in Santa Fe proper, is a little more intense without ever feeling oppressive, and as I'm only in this area occasionally, I do like to soak up the rays of energy. And watch the bemused faces of passersby, many of whom are getting their first taste of one of the country's playfully wacky hidden gems, creations made by people who know they are lucky to have found each other in this world.

She exits with Wilma and Travis. Elsye speaks for all. "Hey they were gonna head over to Tent Rocks for a little hike. Come with? I kinda wanna run something by you." Everything is a free-for-all in Madrid and taking the moment up on its offerings is generally the right way to go. But you have to drive all the way back to Santa Fe to get on the main road that would take you to Cochiti Pueblo, the Indian land on which those rock formations sit. I express as much.

"Oh," Travis laughs, "yeah, we're not going that way. You city slicker." "Yeah, we'll be taking the back roads," Wilma says. I know what that means. These are not roads on a map. Not just unpaved, but untamed. I laugh and put my fingers to my temples, "Okay... I think I can deal with it." Esmerelda will be sitting this one out. "Let me just get some chocolate at Shugarman's before they close, and then we can go." A top tier chocolatier for any city, their white chocolate lemon ginger hibiscus bark is my favorite; as long as I have that when I return home, the trip is a success. It will compensate me for whatever road trauma may lay ahead today.

We climb into Travis' off-road jeep and get ready to hold on for dear life. I don't actually understand how cars can be made to handle such adversity, with holes in the road that don't seem passable. But these people take pride in it.

As we're bouncing up and down on one particularly perilous stretch of road, Elsye lets out a yelp and Wilma says, "You OK back there Laura?" I thought she didn't remember my name, but Elsye laughs, "Oh I'm enjoying every second!" "Laura?" I yell to her, above the scream of the loud large tires gripping hell with their trajectories. "You didn't know she was Laura?" Wilma yells back, holding her scarf to her head, as Travis shifts gears against the terrain. "Laura Crest!" Elsye nods, "L.C." "Ahh!" I yell back & applaud. "Elsye Sender is my pen name for messaging to the world, but I am that writer, after all, so that's what I go by."

Elsye is just one of those people who finds her own path. I always thought she had an open relationship with her roommate Chuck Crest, because I know Elsye to date women fairly openly, but now I put it together they are brother and sister, sharing space and rent. And that's why they always seem so familiar with each other and somewhat touchy, yet I'd never seen them kiss. And he never showed an ounce of jealousy when she kissed some footloose girl at one of their barbecues. Well, this ride is full of eye openers.

"Whoaa!!" Travis screams, somehow drawing a 'whoa' from all three of his passengers almost by instinct as the jeep leaps into the air off of what must've been a larger rock. "Sorry about that!" he says, getting the path back under control, and we all giggle. It's such an absurd way to roll, slamming against bumps at no slow speed, that you just have to laugh— so long as it's not your car.

The Kasha-Katuwe Tent Rocks is a bit far out from main roads, and once we settle back onto paved path, it's true you pretty much will always catch wild horses galloping across the plains on your way there, and the topography is entirely unique. Like they are called, these formations have the shape of huge pointed tents, that seem like they've been placed there from a 1950s sci-fi movie set, as the Council of High Coned Brain Beings. Again, something seemingly manipulated and constructed, which is entirely naturally occurring, from 6 to 7 million years ago, a product of ancient volcanic activity, and formed from ash, pumice, and tuff deposits over a thousand feet thick.

I always agree to go because it's so dramatic and other-worldly, and yet one of its particular charms for me is that it seems like you're hiking but not really. I mean, I don't love the climb of a hike but this essentially goes at a very slight incline in a big circle. Feels like an adventure but leg work is fairly minimal. And wow does the sun bake off those rocks. Always with a slight breeze and those zero-humidity, bright, good feeling vibes that are particular to the New Mexican climate.

As we set off, boot to terrain, there's a roar of thunder, even though there are few clouds. The summer is Monsoon season, so being a desert doesn't stop it from raining every day for about 10 minutes just after 4 o'clock. It comes out of nowhere and leaves just as fast, except the temperature drops 12-15 degrees, as the desert's own built-in air-conditioning system. Right now, however, it's blazing.

"So Cybilline, what I wanted to run by you, is..." and she hesitates, and kind of squints her face, "is it okay to ask you about a relationship issue I'm having?" "Yeah sure, anything," I tell her. "Hey I got a free ride out to this beautiful place, didn't I?" "A ride, is that what you call it?" Wilma jokes. We're all smiling, and I appreciate that Travis and Wilma don't separate themselves off to create a relationship bubble, as we walk forward.

"I've been with this one girl Mariella for maybe five years, and we have a very tight bond," she says, and immediately starts biting the corner of her thumb nail. "So that's not the girl I saw you with at the barbecue?" "Ah no, no that was... someone else." She and Wilma both laugh, perhaps about something they've talked about before related to her. "Mariella isn't into the scene much. She's a homebody."

"You probably haven't even met her, Cybilline," Wilma interjects, "she's seen with no greater frequency in these parts than the legendary

Bigfoot. But she's a spectacular fit for Miss Party Pants over here," she continues, pulling a drag on her cigarette and aiming it at Elsye. "Don't ya think, Travis?" Meanwhile, I'm finding it humorously curious that she holds a red plastic portable ashtray in her hand to collect the ashes, but then we live in a land where Fire Danger Rating placards are a regular sight along roadsides throughout the state, so this does fit in with local precautions. "I... I really don't pretend to know," he says. Feeling the weight of a desired reply from his mate, he offers a noncommittal, "I suppose so."

"But anyway," Elsye cuts in, wrestling back our focus to her initial line of concern, "obviously we have an open relationship but I just wanna say, I don't see our openness as any lack of commitment to each other," she says with seasoned calm. "We both see it as helping each other grow and explore experiences, and living under the religion of having a good time, you might say." Then she looks more directly at Wilma and relates, "You know it's not about depth of love."

"Look, I ain't sharin' Travis with no one," Wilma says, shaking her head, and adds, "That'll be World War 3 if anyone should try. But you make your own complications." Her hand is raised. "I respect your choices."

"And," Elsye says, now leaning toward me matter-of-factly, "it is the trust we've shown each other through not trapping one another, and the willingness to support each other's exploring, that always made our bond stronger. She appreciates me enough to let me live my fullest life."

"Hey, I am familiar with that experience," I assure her. "I know you are, girl!" she crows back, "that's why I seek your counsel on this matter." Elsye then grabs Wilma's cigarette and says, "Gimme that." As she hands it back, she seems to look at her nails, seeing what may appear worse for the wear, and then shakes off that momentary fixation. "So we had this neighbor move in'ta that green house across from Mariella's, which is three places down from me and Chuck's," a description which, oddly, I can vaguely picture. Her road is too bumpy for Esmerelda's liking and I probably walked by once or twice. "Wait," I ask with sudden recollection, "the place that has those llamas in the yard?"

59

"Just that one Cybilline!" she confirms. "So he's a..." and she looks to Wilma. "He's a man," Wilma says deadpan. "Oh stop," Elsye laughs. "He's a real nice and good-lookin' man. He and Mariella read a lot of the same books, and they hit it off. Heck, I like him myself," she explains. "Yeah? Do ya?" Wilma says with a doubting squint of the eye. Elsye rolls her eyes back like she's been inappropriately cross-examined. "Not like that, and if you haven't noticed, I'm trying to confer here with Cybilline."

Quickly changing expression and tone, she says, "So Mariella wants to sleep with this guy," and cranes her neck as if to say 'ya know?' then adds, "I mean, allow it, if that should happen." I nod that I get it.

"Ravishing as I am and such, why would I care?!" she says, "but ya see, ...bein' right across the street, that boy lives closer to her than I do!" as though this would somehow also determine proximity to the heart. You always find yourself in weird conversations with Madroids, where one half of the conversation are the words spoken, and the other half is some slightly squirrely subtext running afoul of lucid logic. The 'what's going on here' bell is always quietly tapping its chatter somewhere in the background.

"So for my own clarity," I say, "Mariella has always been aware she's bi, and you've also been aware of this." Elsye brushes her finger along the ridge of her nose, up to her eyebrow. "Oh yeah, she's omnisexual and if I were guessing on the long-term plan here, she will want us all to live together in hump-along harmony," Elsye chirps.

"Ahhh" I say, beginning to catch the thread that ties this story together. "And I just love her for having no walls and no need to define, so don't get me wrong," she's quick to clarify. "But I'm experiencing an issue."

I see an eagle circling above, overlooking the area of the entire monument. It enters my awareness as something that's fearlessly free and possessing unquestionable bravery for seizing upon a calculated risk. But thick clouds have followed the thunder and roll in as quickly as if designed for a movie set. I wink at the sky. I get the sense there is enough room for a little more wind beneath those wings to explore without immediate danger lurking.

"Granted, with open relationships, some think there's no jealousy, but of course there is," I say, "but you prioritize the gains over the pains."

"Yeah but jealousy is weirder when it's a guy instead of another girl, because you're not entirely sure if you can compete against a change in body... *equipment*," she says after a pause. "What if she finds she's straighter than she thought!" is the worry Elsye poses with a sudden startle. "I reckon some jump the fence ya know!"

"Fluidity is real," I easily concede. "Hasn't been for me!" Travis finally chimes in with greater commitment to his tenets. "It doesn't for many people," I tell him, though I sense he's never actually given it a shot. "And to your point, Elsye, the dynamics with the opposite sex are also different."

"There's a six-inch difference," she shoots back, "on average." Wilma laughs. "And many a horse race has been won on less than that margin," Elsye adds with an animated expression.

Indeed, I had a client explain to me eloquently that what made him identify as gay wasn't about the sex component quite as much as it was the ability to love. He could enjoy sex with men or women, it was sex after all. But he found he "needed the D" in his words, the physicality of another man's body, to feel complete in his experience of love. That it was indeed the biology of the same sex that attracts, and the romantic attainment thereof necessary to achieve a full sense of bonding. This is in conflict with those who claim the issue is that gender doesn't matter and they love beyond gender and body parts. But the point is, that for many it is indeed determinative. And if that had not been the case, that strict covenant of biology, then he would've simply chosen not to be gay, and happily avoided persecution, where entire families and communities might desert you for having loved differently. The sexual acts being merely an expression of that capacity to form a depth of love, to feel a union.

This is why Mariella's interest in a dalliance with this new guy could potentially be great for their relationship. Tragic, of course, to a couple pursuing a traditional arrangement, but for those adding experimentation to their intimacy mapping, not so. She could emerge a more complete person, even in physical awareness, for having that exploration, and internalize a fuller arc of complexity within the many-chambered heart. And from that, have more to impart to her primary love companion.

"In my head, it does make sense," Elsye confirms. "Is this really any different than what five years of love with benefits has been this whole time," she shares, sweet as an apple pie, with a little tough crust on the edges for good measure. "And so of course, I look forward to whatever the adventure holds. But thing is... thing is," she repeats a bit slower, "I'll admit, my heart in this moment, for some reason, says fuck that," and she laughs with the slight nervous energy of possibly having been found out, even to herself. "And what I keep coming back to is, aren't we supposed to follow our heart?"

"That's right Laura," Wilma says, and then looks over at me. "And I just want to mention, I've known this girl a ways back, and despite their good times together, I'd swear she's a bit of an intimacy phobe."

"Am not," Elsye says defensively. "I'm not picking at you," Wilma comes back, pointing at her, "what I'm saying is you're very taken by Mariella, and have opened yourself up in a different way to her." "Ok fine," Elsye consents. "Maybe somethin' you wanna hold on to," Wilma concludes. Travis dutifully nods in agreement, trying to regain his composure after seeming nonplussed.

I take another quick glance up again at the eagle, who is only flying to higher altitudes now. The clouds have grown wispier but linger further across the expanse of the valley. "I just want to clear up a popular misconception, first. Follow your heart does not mean follow your emotions or thinking with your 'feelings'. Feelings are often like a blind screaming child that needs its hand held, because it feels slighted, insecure, and a host of other reactionary responses. In fact, following your heart sometimes means the opposite of listening to your emotions, and grabbing that screaming baby, legs kicking and all, and dragging it out of the room, so that you can do what the heart knows is the right thing, so it doesn't mess up a situation that is precious to you."

Wilma stops walking this time, and Elsye follows suit, but I just keep on with the talk. "It means allowing the wisdom of love to guide us, not necessarily our feelings," I clarify. "So, thought exercise," I say as gingerly as possible: "Is it your philosophy, albeit worst case scenario, to let the person you love go if they find someone who is better for them. Or would you rather hold on to them anyway." There's no point in pussyfooting around that, because it's the question that jealousy itself has no answer for. Do you place yourself above the other person's wellbeing, and is that love? Not that many live up to the ideals of philosophical romance! But Elsye knows the territory after five years. She squints. Nods her head yes.

"I definitely don't want to lose her," is the obvious admission that spills forth. "And I would not feel right standing in the way of whatever path her heart finds, even though I surely hope I am what it continues to find." I purse my lips with a slight smile in recognition of the feeling. "And you know what, strangely that did help," she says, "because it reminds me that Mariella and I know what we have. And if she said, there's a new dummy in town with a nice shape in his pants, I'd say go and hogtie that boy!" Wilma and Travis can't hold back their laughs.

"Oh dear god," Travis shrieks. "I'm gonna cover your delicate ears," Wilma cackles, wrapping her arms around him from behind. "Point being, why should it matter that she actually likes who he is and not just that he's cute. That's certainly more rewarding," Elsye clarifies, to herself.

"I hear you," I relate, "but some open relationship rules are that you can have sex with whoever but no kissing because the kiss is sharing real intimacy and not just physicality. It's up to everyone to make their own guidelines."

"We are committed to each other's growth and exploration," she says, "and to be a support to the other in whatever we go through, and to love each other doing it." I raise my eyebrows with respect at her commitment to even be able to articulate that. "Those are our rules," she says, almost with a lump in her throat, which further touches me. I wonder if Wilma still thinks she's less committed to her relationship simply because she weaves her connectivity by a different design.

I am wearing fitted bell bottom pants with a scarf that I've sewn down the leg, which shimmies in a gust of wind, like a flag that's been planted into the earth. I watch Elsye notice the wave of the fabric, which reading her eyes, she seems to take as a release from a weight that has been enwrapping her. It suddenly gets so bright as the clouds pass, we are all squinting to adjust.

"Elsye, one long term observation," I suggest, cupping my hand over my eye to be able to see her properly against the sun's glare. "There are countless seeming-scenarios in life whose answer is just Believe In You."

She fist-pumps with me, and catching the light now hitting her eyes, I can see some cloud cover has indeed cleared, though there's still some water in those lids. "And since we're just walking in a big circle anyway," I offer as we embark past the midpoint of our short hike, "there's really no destination..." I shrug, "but lots of little beauties."

"I say yes to it all and ask for no guarantees," Elsye states as if issuing a declaration. She performs a little twirl. She giggles. "And I walk..." she says, making Egyptian hand motions, moving forward in an ancient dance. She captures all our attention, with the abracadabra gestures of the rare mime who charms. Continuing right on cue, "...free of expectations." She has transitioned past the clouds and rejoins the sunshine. She blows on her finger as if to put out a candle's flame.

Now there it is at work, the uses of creativity. Not confined simply to the purposes of artmaking, but we see those same elements at play in determining personal identity and by some extension, our destiny. In each conundrum is a pathway to paint an unexpected reply, like the alchemy that turns lead into gold. Every mind is an artist in how we make sense of our life, the array of possibilities we allow to spring up like little desert flowers along the footpath. This is the poetic way, and wherever Elsye is headed, she's certainly living it.

"Amen to that!" Wilma sends back at her, with arm extended. "What'chu think about that, Travis?" she calls over to her man, issuing unknown challenges. "You keepin' expectations?" But he has returned to the realm of the silent and noncommittal.

One of the duties in our engagement with consciousness, it seems, is this rewriting of the original script on all that emotional programming that lives in the darkness of our unexplored caves. In that, we could live without mentally aging at all, but tragically so, staying children.

And such strong feelings arise to protect us from changes, threats, to our original assumptions. We tell ourselves the trickster of emotion is secretly holding a truth we need to honor... when in fact often what needs respecting is our inner adult. Impassioned outbursts certainly do make more noise, shaking more violently. The attention getter, but often also the concealer. Because it doesn't make those feelings, or the adjustments they demand of us, any more valid or correct, for all their drama. Just as there are viewpoints without merit, there are plenty of misguided passions. There's always a balance to find between thought and feeling, and we must be willing to climb into quite rocky territory to navigate it.

An interesting characteristic to notice at Tent Rocks is that none of these rocks surfaces are smooth, like most stones which have jagged but still soft spots; all of it is rough terrain. And some go much higher than others, with the layers of time visible on those formations along the ridge, marks viewable to the naked eye, measuring nature's battle scars. But the cone shapes tell an unmistakable story, that each formation has been through elemental struggle. And for their trials, each is unique and feels like its own contained completeness, even among so many others like them.

Later, heading back to the city with Esmerelda's warm familiar timbre beneath me, there is yet another of those beautiful sprawling Santa Fe sunsets. The thing is, it will all go by so quickly. We must appreciate our long view, and the wind in our hair.

RADIO REPORT: — "A Thousand Suns" by Casker— plays across the color tones in the sky.

SEQUENCE SEVEN

The movie is not romantic in a romance kind of way. It's romantic in living a life beyond the norm kind of way, which— if you're the adventuring type, is considerably better. And it features a distinctly New Mexican kind of eccentric, meaning a person who goes out and does what no one else has even thought of, and follows their strange individual curiosities and impulses into unique territories. Like our state bird the roadrunner: colorful, quirky, funny, and a model outsider.

Impressively, Angus has reprieved his wearing of the fringe tassel belt that had first caught my eye, and this time a necklace of skulls, feathers, and mini dice, structurally arranged in a way that recalls a horse harness; a degree of unabashed kink I take note of. I can also appreciate that he has picked a film that would solidify a bond of recognition between our spirits, an appreciation for the off-center yet driven by a calling, and while I might add, in no way sexy, a film about a guy digging with his bare hands and moving them in circular motions into the holes of soft, pliable turf. And Angus picked his moments craftily to reach for my hand sparingly and rub with purposefully well-timed acumen between my digits.

"Cavedigger" is about Ra Paulette and yes, he digs caves. But with no power equipment or electricity. He digs them with his bare hands, and rudimentary tools like scraper, shovel, pick... not so different from the tools used by Homo Habilis in the early stone age— to bring shape to his canvas, providing dimension, being accessible to touch. With no drawings or blueprints, and working for a craftsman's $20 wage, he builds massive, artistic, magnificent caves in the solidified sand dune material that is unique to the Ojo Caliente region of New Mexico, an hour north of Santa Fe. The composition of this land allows him to build these structures that, it is theorized, could not be built anywhere else. And there's nothing like them. With his hand-made squiggles, he creates art you can live in. If Dr. Suess were alive, he would have made a book about Ra, and no doubt called it something like "CASTLES in the SAND (By JUST This BARE HAND!)" complete in rhyming anapestic meter. Few could be adapted to a cartoon incarnation of themselves as easily, which I say only to flatter.

Part of what was refreshing was that despite dealing with constant uncertainty, even of knowing for sure whether the material of the cave would always hold, his desire to pursue the muse at any cost drove him forward, and without any hint of complaint against circumstance. You can resent the work of having to pave a path that doesn't exist yet— but not if you're interested in being a trailblazer.

Clocking in at just 40 minutes, this film night out was a strict appetizer. Angus showed up at CCA on a Honda motorcycle, year 1976, a time before his birth... which means here's another guy who knows how to fix things with his hands. He had received a text that some friends were playing pool over at The Cowgirl, so being enough of an autophile to pick the classic car over my riding on the back of his motorcycle, we decide to consolidate by jumping into Esmerelda and heading over. I'm thinking I can grab a frozen margarita to keep my increasing hunger at bay, while dutifully agreeing to let them play this one round. Granted, I cringe a little at this slow old-timey game of hustlers and bored drunks, but I get it— it's a boy thing. And the part where they chalk up the cue stick, and that particular bending arch of the back before striking the ball, is all very sexy. I mean, the heart of pool at the bar is boys greasing these outsized sticks, looking at the table like prey, slapping the balls into holes with a pounding thud, and I am certain there's an unconscious effect of that which increases as one gets drunker and drunker, towards the libidinous.

  RADIO REPORT: — "Fall in Love with Me" by Iggy Pop—plays over the pool hall speakers.

It occurs to me as he's enacting this boy performance ritual that we could grab some lamb burgers to-go from Joseph's Culinary just up the street since we only got dessert there last time, and drive up to my place to paw over art books in the living room. Angus is one of the lead artists at Meow Wolf, our local-gone-national group of upstart artists making quite wild immersive and interactive installations. And while they are known for polygamous marriages, rampant bisexuality, and naked LSD parties, all of which is darling, it is my experience that intimate art book conversations are both an aphrodisiac to an artist, and a sure way to quickly get to know his sensibilities, beyond the facades, because those images open the stained-glass cathedral of the heart, the true source of creative arousal.

When we get to my place, I turn on a variety of lamps and head straight for the kitchen to pour Mr. Angus Hannigan a drink. It's a recipe that features lavender infused vodka, which I've made myself from the lavender plant in my backyard. The recipe has come to the world out of the pages of Ian Fleming's first James Bond novel, Casino Royale. Yes, literature can spill out into life and literally fill our cups. Lavender is so plentiful around Santa Fe, that it's a staple scent and flavor here, known for its mood enhancement. There's the Purple Adobe Lavender Farm, and three competing cafes with locally made lavender ice cream used for affogatos with two shots of espresso; one of those culinary competitions that everyone benefits from! There's even a CBD Lavender Hemp Honey made locally that's one of those dreamy things you can't comprehend until you've put spoon to mouth.

"Wait, what are you reading?" he calls over to me, grabbing a book on my mantle. "Pleasure Slave" is the title, complete with its cover art clearly marketed to draw attention from gay male readership. "Yes, I read gay male pulp fiction— Who do you think has the best idea of what can be done to a male body." His jaw drops. Then his eyes become ignited with something between intrigue and admiration... "You really do read gay male porn?!" He chuckles with a hint of comfortable dismay and shakes the book in his hand.

"I like to learn from the pros," I say with a shrug.

And then as he's settling into the couch, I return with art books, Jonas Mekas film stills, Stephen Morse photographs, Dennis Larkins 3D relief paintings, and I place a couple on the floor, including a commemorative book on the love affair of Serge Gainsbourg and Jane Birkin, a coupling that produced some of the most sensuous French pop music of the 60s. Then I place two more books on the arm of the sofa, a Henry Darger, and flip open to a favorite page of a book on Cy Twombly, an artist who specializes in leaving sections of canvas open and untouched, that communicate that nothing is ever finished and always in process. Then quickly return to the kitchen to bring over our drinks and those lamb burgers. They come topped with sheep's milk cheese and sacrilegiously, I leave the green chile off.

People here of course say you're missing out on the cherished Southwestern sensibilities like the heat of red and green chile, which are truly the pride of New Mexico. The local obsession ranks up there with Love, God, Country, Chile. I place art above all of those things, so we all set our priorities. But point being, they fail to recognize that one can also be missing out on the pleasure of NOT being into something! I am sometimes moved to near exhilaration by the joy felt from taking special note of the entire lack of chile found anywhere on my plate.

  RADIO REPORT: — "33 GOD" BY BON IVER— PLAYS ON MY VICTROLA 1950S VINTAGE STYLE BLUETOOTH JUKEBOX.

After some enthusiastic viewing, and extended eye contact, I go to refresh our glasses, and also light a tea candle under a little bowl that heats up some essential oil of vetiver and jasmine, which I pour in gently. I catch Angus glancing over with curiosity. This will need just a few minutes to warm, and to enhance my own vivacity, I quickly squirt one dropper of 'Secrets of the Tribe' brand Mucuna for myself into a short shot glass of water, finger stir and swig. On a hunch, I quickly seek out something of a textile variety from the bedroom, before returning to Angus sitting on the floor next to the couch.

As he stands, looking at the pages of a book, he surprises me that he's picked up Francis Bacon's "The Brutality of Fact" and is reading interview segments with the artist instead of looking at the pictures. I get behind him and place two fingers with the warm oil on the back of his neck. The warmth is key, to show you've taken time to care, after all... He leans his neck back into my fingers, and surprises me again, by unbuttoning his shirt and sliding it off, to offer more surface area to whatever I might have in mind. How quickly a flame becomes a fire with these young studs.

Luckily, I've brought in my best burgundy jute rope, that is specially crafted for use in the practice of kinbaku. No simple game of tie and titillate, this kind of Japanese rope fetish is a true sensual art form, known as much for its artfulness of tying than for bed games of control and confinement. The knots and patterns applied are aesthetically pleasing and when placed by a virtuoso as such that I've become, each ligament is stretched slowly, tied and sculpted into the desired position. The end goal is a joyous submission, but it's more like the weaving of strands in a web, as an erotic process. It appears Angus is eager. I know he will find liberation in bondage, while, like an art book for the body, heightening his pleasure with the complexly stylized finger dance of tying, mixed with my softly spoken negotiations into his waiting ear, intentionally brushing the tip of my nose in teasing conjunction to his lower lobe, bringing forth sure elation to his already endorphin-engorged brain.

A mere hour goes by and Angus is fully roped. I thoughtfully tip his virile frame to lean him on his right quads, so he's comfortably placed against my wooden throne chair, made for me by a masterful craftsman in Taos, with long flowing hair and angelic optics. Freely allowing me to entirely restrain him so early in the process of knowing each other shows a touching trust between us. I go to my captive and put my hand under his taught jaw. "I've got to run out to the store... Think you can behave?" He looks up into my eyes with a gaze of complete serene subservience, tied up with his left leg spread outward from the front base of the chair, and arms behind him, but still revealing a captivating shape of the shoulders, and other various contours of allure and male magnetism, he slowly nods his head yes. Even tied up and under complete control to be physically maneuvered at will, stripped bare of all but the scantest of covering, he still contains the undercurrent of a dangerous power. I close the door and make my way to the car to fetch some milk from the store. In the morning, I'll make him pancakes.

Esmerelda starts up with extra zeal tonight, whinnying with the confidence of a thousand horsepower engine. I know I just tied up this fetching dreamboat, but there is a much greater bondage concerning me now. As someone who cannot fathom the curtailing of freedoms, except by the strictest of mutual consent, the idea of a seat belt is morally repellent. Falling under the category of cramping style, at minimum, I do not consent. This atrocity to free movement must be abolished!

How would I not notice, as Angus rode his motorcycle to the movie, that there's no seatbelt on that thing! It's more dangerous by design than any form of driven craft could be, but we allow that because it is part of liberty to do so. The autonomous free choice of the human animal. For what possible reason should I be told by governing authorities how much safety I must take, beyond following an agreed speed limit and basic signal protocols. Whose decision is what I do with my body? Apparently someone can decide to be a boxer and get their brains pulverized round after round, for years on end, producing sure irreparable long term damage. But I can't simply choose between electing whether to wear a seatbelt or having freedom of movement inside the cabin of a vehicle I occupy only by myself.

And I fully understand that there are terrified, traumatized people out there in the world who take great solace in such a law, but that controlling fear should remain between them and their therapist. Next we'll be breaking a law to not wear gloves on account of possible frostbite. Do my fingers belong to the government? Where does the jurisdiction on the pursuit of happiness in our own basic choices end? Thankfully, I maneuver with grace, free of this indignity. But I must hurry back to finish up with Angus. After all, he can't be left to wonder for too long, all tied up and such.

My mind drifts. This weekend there are hoop dances at the Poeh Cultural Center for their summer festival and as I drive, I'm making a mental note to make time for it. A big part of the pleasure of living in Santa Fe is the proximity to and interaction with Native American culture. The pueblos don't let you photograph or video their dances, on those occasions when the public is invited in to watch, and because the dances serve religious purposes, even applause after the dancing is not appropriate. Not so at any of the events at Poeh, which are specifically geared toward public enrichment, being itself a cultural museum.

The hoop represents the circle of life, having no beginning or end, but my endless fascination is more with the clothing than even the dexterity of the dances. Brazenly mixing and clashing colors, the way of dress is similar to how you would make a painting, with reds, blues, yellows, and then a splash of orange down by the boot, with beadwork, ribbons, feathers— all spinning in the rush of a human kaleidoscope. So different from traditional western approaches to dress and presentation, the Indians fearlessly evoke the regal.

Even when in full headdress, I don't consider that look exotic but a normal sensible every day aesthetic to express an inner spirit. 'T-shirt and jeans' is much more foreign to me. I turn off the engine and close the car door behind me, and take a moment of leisure to appreciate the ever-present light breezes that continually remind us life is in motion, and that fill the atmosphere with such subtle colognes. The airiness of the troposphere is part of the vibrational lightness so pervasive in this state. Nowhere in all my travels is the feeling of life's sweet enjoyment so much just "in the air" as it is in this area.

I believe, I think as I turn the front door key, that I will start on Saturday at the Tesuque Village Market for their croissant French Toast, and of course pick up a few fresh bits of pastry from their bakery cabinet, before driving up to Poeh. One pleasure leading to another, each building upon subtle elations like a mountain is ascended— but without the tiresome need to climb.

When I open the door and put my groceries down, I walk over to Angus just as casually as turning on a light switch and then slowly loosen his bondage. His speed to passion is immediate. Like he'd been restrained for twenty odd years instead of just twenty minutes, waiting for this singular expression of the clock to finally find release.

With his hands around my waist, he pulls me toward his outstretched mouth and makes an abrupt grunt, but the first thing that reaches me as I near him is the imprint of his manly approval upon my leg. He recognizes this and without missing my reaction of surprise, holds my gaze a beat or two further, and curls a smile of confident showmanship, as if to say "And now?" Well, I can't say I made him wait any longer than that.

Our mouths touch like two shapes increasing the geography of the other, and I feel his facial scruff gently brush my cheek, the way a cloud's shadow lays cover across a biding mountainside. As our geologies merge and vibrate, his breath is warm then hot, similar to the techniques of light. As tongues congeal, the sun's rays erase all barriers and obscure boundaries.

We lay across the soft feel of the urban distressed leather couch, a bundled blend of angling legs and the soothing whispered sounds of exaggerated breathing. The night twists and inclines, while I feel Angus slowly gathering ashes, learning the ways of fire. And for all the talk of men, the potion he concocts is bold; he proves adept at more subtle liaisons, that of voice and hair and eyes and arm.

Of dilated pupil by way of dopamine and oxytocin, and the erecting of every color with his drawing compass, purposefully swinging jagged circles. And with utensil and adroit finger, he takes full and accurate measure of all he enters.

Recurring are moments of stillness and motion, of exhaling and anticipation. As we slowly come down from the pendulum waves and their many shifting articulations, my lips on his neck, I watch him eye the wall, on which hangs a pipe with attached feathers. I smile watching him put together the suggestive invisible smoke signals sent by this dangling temptress. I don't say a word. He squints, then turns his neck to kiss my forehead, and pulls upward to gain his balance and reach his feet. A jangling of his belt as he pulls his pants back up. I'm duly entertained as Angus instinctually takes the decorative pipe off my wall, taps a finger inside the bowl to discover the moist weed he sensed was in there, now identifying the practical purposes of the hung arts.

"You're something else," he says with a pleased giggle. "Got a light? Wait, I have one." He quickly fumbles through his bag and finds what he's after. "Not just for show, I see..." he grins.

One of the feathers on the pipe is damaged, where only half of it remains. But I always took the broken feather to be about imperfect flight and how it's often in our wounds that we make the adjustments we would not have otherwise made, that bring us to more substantive heights. A unique journey being better than any idea of a perfect one. I'll never try to fix it.

Imbibing in some incandescent Santa Fe herb grown by my neighbor Joss, he lays back down, wedging between our intersecting legs, and starts passing the pipe back and forth. We conclude the night watching Jean Luc Godard's masterpiece "JLG/JLG: Self Portrait in December" on an old VHS tape. We fall asleep with the TV shuddering in static noise.

I wake in his arms on the couch at 1:21 AM, and slowly pull away to fetch a chunky knit merino wool blanket that I acquired from Lithuania, because the aesthetic idea of blanketness should reign over any practical aspects of warmth, even in summer. But with the fan offering a cooling cross ventilation between the living room and kitchen windows, I place the luxuriant covering over Angus' quietly exposed and attractively tattooed shoulder. Then, like air, I slink soundlessly into the bedroom and softly close the door behind me.

After removing the top to the jar by the bedside table, in only a matter of moments, a warm sparkling light emanates around the corners of the bedroom door, illuminating its frame.

SEQUENCE EIGHT

Therapy session: Cecilia always sits in the lounge chair, looking out the window. She talks, ruminates, and answers questions, but she feels it gives her more access to the internal when she's not directly engaging with eye contact.

"I am of two minds about it," she says. "I'm excited, even thrilled, and can't wait for the finished product. I'm like a schoolgirl with a crush, waiting for my date to arrive. But then, it's as if I'm nervous of my appearance. I mean, if no one is going to respond to it, why should I make it? This is my dilemma."

"If someone wants something to exist in the world, it's a good thing to pursue that," I calmly suggest.

"Even if it feels like I'm the only one who ends up appreciating it?" she reiterates.

"Aren't you a person and doesn't your experience of your life matter?" I question. "Would you ask yourself if it was worth making a pancake if you're going to be the only one to enjoy it?" I let the silence skittle fry the thought to a crisp brown edge, before adding, "I think you matter."

She allows the growing pause, then starts, "What if you slaved for months making that pancake, processing the grains yourself by hand to make the flour, putting your heart and soul into each ingredient of the recipe and no one cared when you put it out there on the plate."

"Did you enjoy the pancake?" I ask. I pause and draw a little circle for myself resembling a pancake in my notebook, adding wings before continuing.

"And why must others care about your pancakes?" As I speak, I'm wondering why the act of giving must so often be so intimately connected to needing.

Admittedly taking this line of questioning has me recalling my own special pancake recipe, involving Madagascar bourbon vanilla extract, lavender extract, crushed berries, and pine nuts. And how often I am overjoyed to appreciate them alone, and with no one knowing of my recipe.

"...as long as I enjoy them?" Cecilia wonders aloud, as she engages the parallel.

I let her sit with her plate of pancakes for another moment. The idea behind Rogerian therapy is that you repeat back to a person what they're saying, so that they hear their own thoughts better. I am modifying that approach by adapting it to an abstracted mirror of what her thought patterns are saying. Applying some aspects of this when working with artists is a good practice because artists tend to live a fair portion of their lives in their imaginations, and sometimes don't process what they're really saying. Sure it made sense in their head, in that private internal conversation, but hearing it reported back to them, out loud, they often say "What? No!" While never taking away from them the key ingredient of well-being, to discover the solution by, at least what feels like, their own insight.

Cecilia was a successful editor earlier in life, and now is focused on making paintings, which she is both excited about and yet not entirely at ease with all that goes with it. She sells more of her pottery coffee mugs and I have one in the kitchen. I think she does great work with that and I love drinking out of it, because it's beautifully textured and drinking from it is a connection to her— but it's never enough. For most, in truth, whatever art form we indulge is ultimately for us. For our development, a tool for connectivity to our psyche and in mapping our place within ontological existence. It's a form of rooting. But for many people, this lack of recognition for doing the stuff of living well, feels as an unbearable compromise to the ego. Which shows how delusional our relationship to our creations and our personal power has become, as we infuse media-influenced drivel into our worldview, most specifically by the construction of fame, and all its false expectations and the perversely skewed reactions it engenders. That our sense of value is derived from how much attention our creations bring us, allowing profit defined metrics to leak out of the economic system shell it was meant to be contained within, and infect our relationship to spirit. It's like desiring attention for the act of breathing.

"Ok Cybilline," Cecilia says abruptly, "I just want to state that this is absurd," she starts to giggle. "Firstly, because I haven't had a pancake in 10 years." So much for sharing the recipe. She playfully swats her wrist.

Pretending such a loose metaphor is in any way literal is to leave the pancake unchecked so long as to potentially burn the delight of its flavor entirely away. But it often takes mulling over ideas in private to finally, often weeks later, let them seep in with a careful undressing. The truth is, we tend to like our confinements because they comfort us. Who gets hurt in a cage? It's when you roam free that you're in danger.

"Pancakes or pizza for that matter," she continues, holding up her finger to make a point, "...all those breads," and then directs it to her stomach. "That's how I keep this tummy so flat. I haven't indulged for years."

"Sorry for your loss," I say with a little smile, to properly mourn the dead.

In truth, Cecilia is one of those very thin people that make you wonder if there ever was a voluptuous stage— she's physically forever fourteen in body shape. But how often have I heard references like that lately; super thin people that speak of all the joys they deny themselves for fear of getting 'fat' ...but where is their fear of being shallow? It's easy to overlook that being shallow hurts your mental health in greater degrees than a few excess pounds hurts your physical health. And wise to note, studies show that shallowness affects perception of physical attractiveness too.

"But I get what you're saying," she relents, "and I wonder if it could all really be ego, or is it even loneliness, that makes us want to connect and be acknowledged. To not... just eat pancakes ourselves."

I smile that she's lightening up and transferring her awareness toward a solvable existential tension. She smiles while looking out the window, and then sighs, "Why can't I just be Frida Kahlo?"

I wonder how she'd deal with having that fat husband Diego, considering her attitudes about body. Being Frida has so many facets.

"But case in point, you're talking about ignored genius," I say. "Frida Kahlo, Bach, Kafka, van Gogh, William Blake, Edgar Allen Poe, so poor he burned his furniture to keep warm. But these people have spoken to time, the true giants of their art forms, all overlooked their entire lives. And where are those who were popular while they were being ignored? Most of them long forgotten."

This is of course one of the funnier conundrums that so many people buy into, about recognition being tied to a concept of mattering in the grand scheme of things. In the same way, whatever was of tremendous importance in 1872 is as relevant to people today as what we now think is hot and happening will be relevant to those in 2150. It won't. Just a couple of days ago, I showed a picture that I saw on Tumblr to one of the students at St. John's, of about 100 of the biggest stars at an awards show from the mid 1970s. "Who the hell are these people?" he said with a smirk, handing me back my phone. After prodding, he could identify only three of them. What that whole room full of egos would have done if they only could lift the veil just a couple of generations down the line, to how unknown they would be, and not more remembered after all than their siblings and friends, many of whom errantly treated them as royalty. We start as dust, we end as dust.

Meanwhile, Cecilia is nodding her head, agreeing to something in her mind, looking out that window, squinting her eyes.

"Those artists would have been wrong to think they'd failed, Cecilia," I encourage her. "Don't YOU know a musician, a photographer, a dancer, a painter... who you think should be famous beyond belief, and yet just a handful of people appreciate them? But their work... their work, Cecelia... it's spectacular!" I say with enthusiasm and warmth, my eyebrows raised with supportive compassion.

Suddenly she looks at me with a startle. After a quick pause of silence, she says, "I believe I channeled Leonardo da Vinci at my easel last night..." Her eyes beam with intensity. "And do you know what he told me?!"

At that moment, the cuckoo clock, which I keep activated as a kind of therapy-joke to lighten the mood of where some conversations inevitably go, or to lighten the ego because many people's neurosis comes merely from taking themselves too seriously (You're just a breathing sack of cells, after all), lets out 3 cuckoo calls. CUCKOO! CUCKOO! CUCKOO!

"I think your time is up," I say.

"We'll continue with that next time," she replies with eyes bright, "it's a very interesting conversation," suddenly carrying a light sparkle about her, as she grabs her handbag.

I have just moments before my next client, so I go to brush my hair, and put my yellow stovetop espresso maker on the burner. By the time it rings out, Billy has arrived. Looking out the window, I see a red-faced warbler perched on the top of the Coyote fence, popular enclosures in Santa Fe made of cedar polls, which surrounds the yard. With its bright color, this little bird never hides its splendor. But also never asks any applause for its plumage either.

Billy needs a quick bathroom break upon arrival, so I stay at the window.

As I pour the coffee into the mug Cecilia made, what would be so amazing to me is if she could grow to see that it can actually be cool to be unappreciated, to be an outsider. What a revolution in her consciousness that would be. I still maintain that there is a "Stairway To Heaven" unknown laying around in someone's closet of unrecorded songs, that the world will never know. In fact, I listened to a Sun Ra album just this morning, the first side of "The Soul Vibrations of Man", rare even among his lesser-known albums, and it was so extraordinary. Here's a man who self-released over 200 albums on privately pressed vinyl at a time when record companies ruled, so interested was he in creation rather than the mechanics of acclaim. But I could either think "How sad so few know of this"— or instead be thankful there are still a few beautiful secrets left. The more saturated with information, all the same information, we become, perhaps more and more, our joy will come from having a magic album to walk into, that feels more our own, because everyone else doesn't know about it, and that we can share it with just a special friend we believe will receive the connection, as a bond just between us.

The way things work, when you're an original, or you're ahead of your time in any way, it very often means people aren't ready to see it yet and that they probably won't. If you invent to be brilliant enough to go over people's heads, why would you be upset when it succeeds in doing that? It would definitely be more interesting to be a filmmaker like Harry Smith with his cutout animation and hand-painted films featuring mystical symbolism, which are true personal masterworks, than any Hollywood director with their films playing at strip mall movie theaters, no matter how many awards they may garner. But being a Harry Smith won't make you a living.

To be comfortable being an outsider is to occupy a powerful place of honesty, partly because you will go misunderstood by many. Even the occasional success will likely go misunderstood. It's like Rudolph the Red-Nosed Reindeer. We have all grown up with this story, but in actuality it's told from the position of the normative and ungifted, not the odd and exceptional. I hate to break it to those who love this cherished fable, but when you're a Rudolph kind of entity, you don't give a shit about fitting in with other reindeer and being part of their idiot games. You're too busy rocking out your amazing red nose. You've got your own answer, your own connection to the divine. So it was written from the perspective of the squares. What they did get right in that story is that he was underappreciated and not understood by the popular culture he existed within, and that he steps up into his power and saves the day one fateful night, when it's needed. But you can spare him the pity party. I can assure you Rudolph the Red-Nosed Reindeer never cared about what you thought or fitting into your little social clique.

That said, my nose does suddenly feel a touch dry! Living in the desert especially can play havoc with your sinuses, with anything that requires moisture. I drop a little Nasya oil on a Q-tip, and sooth the inner portions of my nasal passages. Looking at my counter, I grab the lavender oil and rub in just a dab onto my chest to open my lungs. There are little things you can do throughout the day to always be optimal.

I look over at the dark green vial of ChlorOxygen for a little hit of energy, but Billy emerges just then, a little sweaty. "Are you alright, Billy?" I ask.

"It really is torture, I think, at times," he says, wiping his brow. "I just can't get away from my thoughts. I was in the studio since 6 AM and just trying to get something exactly right, detail to detail. So I need a second to get my brain out of that cave so I can talk with you and be present."

He's been working with glass using a process that makes the material soft like flower petals, and places these pieces onto canvas, in a form that resembles energy painting. Labor intensive and more interesting to me than the work he was once known for, it's the first time he's stepped out of a box of familiarity, and concurrently, he's been on edge for the past few months as he tries to adjust, with my encouragement.

"Here, I just made some espresso actually, let me give you some and we can start by chatting casually and work our way in." I hand him a cup and saucer.

Billy is one of those artists that caught the wave at a time, and while the work he is making now is no less compelling, his abiding inner struggle is that for a number of years he had real recognition, simply by matching the zeitgeist of the moment, like a child who jumps into frame at just the moment a photographer snaps his picture, and that image travels around the world, a snapshot represented as a moment of significance in history. Though again, the kid was simply just passing through. Fate took it from there.

I used to volunteer at the Whitney Museum back when I lived in New York, and fortunately the tours go through the Education Department, so it's a real bird's eye into how high culture is constructed. Not necessarily by the quality of the work, but on the whims of the gallerists and curators who seek to tell a certain story at the moment and find the artists that conform to that, or are willing to create work within the parameters of those themes. The Biennials were notorious for this practice. Not the best of now, but the best at conforming to the narrow lens the curator decides to present it under.

In a lecture we hosted, a very famous photographer was on a panel and she mentioned that the entire mythology around her work was not something she had ever said herself. "It may or may not be true in certain instances," she informed us, "but my point is that I myself never said that of my work." It was invented for her, to build the mystique around her photographs, that could be used to sell that to wealthy patrons. Generally by the time it makes its way up to the Museum level, it's already been vetted and the "creation stories" of the artists, formed— but there was plenty of myth making in building exhibitions as well. That's of course a post-modern problem; if you told van Gogh that ten pages of essay text would be needed to explain why what he'd made was art, he'd tell you to fuck right off.

Alas as simple timing brings people in and out of fortune in an almost random roulette, Billy now lives in the shadow of his glory years, even though the hoopla that surrounded him was a throw of the dice. There is no validity to the notion that the 'successful' work was better than what he now creates, but it feels that way because there had once been applause. He shows awareness of the dynamics of the trap he is in, but very little of how the psychological cage behind it is of his own making.

"The trouble is that you become successful, which people think they want, and are expected to make that same thing over and over. So your success is a quagmire, because the same process that got you to discover this 'thing' you get known for, is something you engage in less and less. Instead of exploring the unknown, you explore the known: what people want and expect from you. And this is less satisfying, but it puts food on the table. And let's face it, doesn't hurt the ego either to be written about in ARTnews."

Or in his case, the memory of being written about in ARTnews 15 years ago. The attachment to the outside world, even when proven illusory, is still that strong.

There is no doubt that most artists' displeasure with their lot in life has to do with connecting their creations with a way to get out of having a job, other than just doing what's on their canvas or being up on a stage. Even though less than 1% succeed in doing that. Meanwhile, it is not so difficult to have the stability of a job, one that doesn't take too much out of you to have the energy and time to devote to making what you love. That route would allow experimentation in a way that keeps one challenged and fulfilled, without ever dancing to other people's demands when it comes to the nuances of your art.

And worth asking, are you more of a professional for putting your art in that precarious relationship to commerce, or might the more serious artist be the one who refuses to do that, and takes supplemental employment instead?

It's easy to forget the astounding pluses that the simple act of artmaking can give your life. One must first consider that most people just have to live with whatever other people create for them to enjoy, whether it's a TV show or the music they listen to; they are stuck with those options created by others. But an artist can manifest anything from their imagination into the world, and bring their innermost visions alive. If you're a musician, you might be able to write something that becomes your favorite song in the world. What a glorious private accomplishment! So there is almost an audacity, after having that advantage to enjoyment, to complain.

Remember that most of human history has existed without recorded music; a world where people had to sing together, or to play instruments, if they wanted the joy of music in the home, much less Immediate Access to the Finest Musicians of Modernity, recorded in the greatest studios, with years of production value to get a song just right, which can be heard at the mere touch of a button. How are any of us unhappy, when given that level of access to inspiration.

And of course I'm being a little cheeky, but my point is the degree to which so many little gifts —all around us and inside us— are taken for granted. It's certainly my role to preserve self-esteem and foster some illusions in doing so, but the frequency of this simple thought about the dynamics of observational gratefulness does recur for me.

The door closes, the door opens. In walks Ann. She doesn't come to sessions because something's wrong but because something's right. She sees therapy as a healthy activity for her just like working out or meditating or traveling. Now in her early 80s, she has no uncertainty causing her emotional entropy, but is ready to greet every day with her full self, it seems, and is still freeing herself into new territories.

"I've really been getting into perceptions versus reality," she says with excitement. "I've been looking at a lot of online porn."

"Oh!" I say. "Yes, I discovered quite accidentally on Twitter that Twitter has porn! And lots of it." "I did know that," I say without abashment. I find Tumblr provides that in a much more artful rewarding context, but I don't think this is the moment for that share-out. "I've been with my fair amount of men and they all seemed in a relative range in size differences in terms of men's, you know" and she lifts her hands to make a shape but then thinks better of it, and then lowers her hands and then lifts her hands and lowers them again. She shakes her head charmingly and continues: "But anyway, I've learned it's considerably more variant than I thought. It's just like flat chested women and then H Cup. I never knew that! A giant spectrum, ranging from a coffee stirrer to a vacuum hose." I raise my eyebrows lightly and shake my head yes at this quite profound truth that she has come to. "And as I investigate this, I find that some of them have channels where they make money, showing it off in videos!" she exclaims. "Like the peep show rooms you'd find in some seedy areas of big cities."

"You don't say?" I feign unawareness. "And let me tell you, Cybilline... it's almost the next sexual revolution. We're turning a corner. Things like Twitter allows everyone to be a porn star from their bedroom. Boys and girls alike making money on their bodies. You know, 'I have a hot body, send me money' thing. But I don't judge! It's a new world. And WHAT BODIES!" She places her hand on her mouth, like she's spilled the beans about her best friend's affair. "Well..." she continues, "it just shows that even the biggest porn stars of the past were not really that impressive when you consider what's inside the undergarments of some of these fellas!" She spreads her hands wide like floodgates.

"They really measure up, huh?" I say, now more convinced she is going through something and fascinated to see where we'll end up with this topic. And yes it's true, the kind of erotic allure once promised only by rock stars is now found just scrolling through your phone screen. Not people doing pornos, just people dropping their drawers and shaking their dangling trophies to behold and view for the camera, those who would never have pursued contractual nudity. Kinsey would have ended up with much more staggering results had he been performing his sex studies nowadays. It's also why bisexuality is enjoying such a well-earned renaissance. The access level to exploring any fascination with sexual physicality, that used to require an in-person visit to a naughty video or book store, allows people to simply explore what is true for them, from an earlier age. And to see others exploring it too. And why not?

"So I've had a surprising amount of realization around this..." She smooths out her skirt before continuing. Her black widow spider necklace flashes from the spark hitting it through the window's light, and I pretend it's an intentional act of magic power on her part, to make the moment feel even more compelling. "Things which seem a turn on, in fantasy, something hot, say, in a porn context, may actually not be desirable in real life. But I'm allowing a level of visual stimulation to infiltrate my psyche." She pauses and her eyes become more charged with energy. "The kind of imagery I used to fight, and place decency restrictions on for what's acceptable. I didn't even know I was repressed! And I really think I am breaking through that."

"Like?" I say, putting my pen to my lips and leaning forward. She takes a sip from her water bottle and lifts her head.

"Maybe I'm having trouble articulating this. But art is visual and porn is visual," she starts, and I say "uh-huh" trying to follow. "Some porn turn-ons express power dynamics between two people I might not find acceptable in my own bedroom; real sex to me is emotional and visceral. But I feel I'm strengthening my relationship to my visual vocabulary, the art realm, by permitting what I once denied myself, through peeping at these images, seeing such bodies in motion. You know, allowing symbolic, once forbidden energetics... to enliven."

"Ahhhh I get it. So you're holding the primal energy of the once hidden but now unsheathed phallus in your mind as a libido enhancement and allowing that lust of the object and its form, as a boost to your own creative power," I say, energizing myself by the idea, "like adding some rocket fuel." She nods yes with a pleasing smile. "Rocket fuel that had been missing," she says quietly. "Ann, I think this is a beautiful breakthrough and I so support you in that." After a moment of replay in my mind, I add with full assurance: "These are your doors to open."

The door closes and opens again. Jerome is lonely. He's been in New Mexico two years. Something about the dream of Santa Fe makes people think they can just jump into it and start living here. Thing is, you actually have to like yourself to make it in Santa Fe, to occupy this space. There aren't enough distractions to keep you from your own psyche and whatever is dwelling in there. No hype to pacify. You will have to deal with you— and for many, that's a very tall ask.

"I'm questioning how much I have to offer. I admit I stay on the surface a lot. I started painting as a way to build connections, like a language, that I didn't necessarily find in speaking with people. But I came from a city, where people were omnipresent. You could be by yourself but didn't fully realize you were never really by yourself. Here, you have to make more of an effort. And my question is, can I do that? I don't know. And I recognize that it's more that I'm hesitant to go further inside myself, because what if there's nothing worthwhile that I'll find. Just... uninspired ordinariness."

The places people put themselves in can be heartbreaking. Like a cat in a tree. Jerome showed me postcards of his paintings in our very first session, and his work is abstract and painterly. It didn't show confident sensory depth like you would see in de Kooning or an ease with inwardness like Agnes Martin, but a pleasant emotional searching. From what he tells me, it was his positive reception on Canyon Road that convinced him to move here. But his art has found a place before he has.

"You like hiking... You know how the further into remote uncharted territory you get, the more exotic the wildlife you discover? Well, that holds true for uncharted spiritual interior territories too. That's where the real glistening energies reside, where you can feel a —pardon the term— 'magical' connection to your existence. And in those places, may gain access to some lightness in your heart. That's something we all need."

"I understand a lot of this comes down to fear," he says, tugging on his ear, "which I need to work through. Art can't live off of itself forever, it needs experiences, it needs life to be lived, to create from. And I just need to get out there, even if it means saying hello."

"It's true," I say, "fears are generally not there to be afraid of, Jerome. They may appear so that they can be stood up to. Fear and pain usually have some kind of information inside them, which means they often have something to teach us, after all... And if there's a challenge, you can make that challenge your friend."

You don't have to be a psychiatrist to prescribe a bottle of reassurance.

"This reminds me, I've had a question I've been meaning to ask YOU," he says, and I ponder his curiosity. "You're so brave in what you wear, you don't hide at all. But that got me wondering, do those strings and fabrics on your clothes have religious significance? For instance, as a protection?" His eyebrows raise.

I look down at my sleeveless blouse with vintage flower applique reappropriated from another shirt sewn just below the bosom, leading to bits of eye-pleasing scrap yarn expertly hanging down the top seam of the waist pocket, and a strip of fabric repurposed from yet another blouse, with perfect white stars against a blue base reminiscent of Wonder Woman herself, stitched down just the left sleeve, to function somewhat like an accent wall but for accentuating the curve of the arm, and I think I may have outdone myself. Truth is, my attire is my way of fighting what the world is; its conformity, its repetitiveness, its lack of humor, its refusal of all that is unique and square-box resistant.

Which can be ironic... because when you're pretty and fashion forward, people don't always see the invention, and even assume vapidity. For sure, there are those who, on first glance, I'm sure mistake me as someone taking the Kool-Aid, rather than the one making the Kool-Aid. And yet a man who works out at the gym to erect a sculpted physique, is never just assumed to be less intelligent or a follower of trends, which that gym look absolutely can be. But fighting what the world is certainly doesn't mean changing what the world is.

"Yes," I say with a pregnant pause, "I find they protect me from mundane normative experience," I confide. "But you know what? Also that being bold often attracts interesting people into starting up a conversation."

"Ahhhhhhhh" he says, eyes opened wide. The door closes again.

It's amazing sometimes how many different quandaries people are in, with relation to their art and process. What none of them —the known or unknown, the celebrated or unsung— want to acknowledge is that truly most of the magic of this world is done behind closed doors, which none will ever see. Is the painting itself the staggering accomplishment or all the moments spent painting it? The victories are personal, not public. But that reality is not where the recognition is. So even though people often don't like the rigors of the ego game, they'd still rather hold onto the illusions of that, than face the endless void of an empty universe that gives no trophies and no reply. But wild thing is, it isn't even remotely empty.

In fact, much dissatisfaction with life can be traced to people interpreting the Moment itself as an Empty thing, needing to be filled up with some action or activity— instead of recognizing the Moment as a Vibrantly Alive Entity, that can fill YOU up. If you'd only rid yourself of the notion that it was dead pointless space in the first place.

SEQUENCE EIGHT-AND-A-HALF

I love to take a drive out to Galisteo on Sundays. It's a small town twenty minutes from my casita, and a part of Santa Fe County that's been continuously inhabited since before 6000 BC, and whose tribal occupants include the Anasazi. Haunted is not a word I would use to describe the remnant feeling of this long history of human occupation upon the land, but there is a stirringly animate energy, of a very beautiful and peaceful nature there. A sense of portals, openings, in the atmosphere. There's even a Space Princess who lives there, who founded a Light Institute. She holds free meditations on Sunday nights and unlocks windows to the sky. Just a little everyday Santa Fean sorcery.

This drive itself is the kind of sanctification of spirit and clearing the mind that some might equate with going to church, but where the church is merely beauty and awe itself. I never tire of the desert scrub, the miraculous quality of light that reveals every angle of each twig in the anatomy of chaparral, causing it to sparkle like a holographic diamond, even as you ramble past them, down Old Las Vegas Highway at untold speeds behind the wheel of a turquoise 1959 Ford Galaxie.

I stop off at Cafe Fina, as it's essentially the last opportunity for coffee before nearing Galisteo Basin, a place without a commercial presence of any kind, and whose residents complain if any outdoor lights are left on at night to spoil the total aura of immersive stargazing. Meanwhile, I'm happy just as long as the lights at Cafe Fina are on, because they have the best pancakes on the planet, which they call "Cloud Cakes", possibly because they deliver your mouth to certain flavor heavens. This local intoxicant has that buttery flavor of a crepe, but still the filling substantiality of a pancake, and yet the crisp edges of the former. How? Clearly by way of magic. I'm sure you have ideas about this, but if there's such an obvious answer, how come no one else can replicate them?

In any case, today is just a quick drive-thru day and as the hatch opens, I catch a glimpse of that boy Ruff who often mans the window. I've yet to figure out what Ruff is short for, but he's the most glorious specimen of a male I have ever seen. Sorry New York! Sorry Paris! Sorry Medellin! Sorry Sydney! Sorry Los Angeles! You may have over 22 million faces across your saucy borders, but you have not one dish as stunning as Ruff. No, the title for most beautiful man I have ever laid eyes on is a perfect embodiment right here in Santa Fe. And he's making me coffee and smiling. By what act of witchcraft could such a creature have been summoned into this unworthy world. I keep making nonsensical noises like a tongue-tied schoolgirl, tripping over my desire to communicate, but in his immaculate grace, he overlooks this, and just keeps smiling back with those angel eyes and angel hair and angel lips. And as God is my witness, angel hips.

"Could you put just a splash of vanilla in there, Ruff?" I ask with doelike innocent tones, "if it's not too much trouble." That light comes shining from his eyes, his cheeks... "You like all the good stuff in there," he calls back. "I doooo," I think, but my mouth doesn't open to say it.

You know, some people like to pretend you couldn't date guys in their mid-20s. What would you possibly talk about? Well, firstly, one look at Ruff and talk is not of uppermost concern. But Bob Dylan was 21 when he wrote "Blowin' in the Wind", Jim Morrison was 22 when he wrote "The Crystal Ship", David Bowie was 22 when he wrote "Space Oddity", Robert Plant was 22 when he wrote the lyrics to "Stairway to Heaven", Pete Townsend was 23 when he wrote The Who's entire rock opera "Tommy", and Lou Reed was 25 when he wrote the literary rock masterpiece, "Heroin". Point is, most of the greatest and most eloquent music in rock 'n' roll history, which are eternal compositions and transcendent performances, were created by young, inspired, brilliant, hot men. And if you wouldn't date any one of these guys, at the very moment and age they wrote those songs, you are a fool. I've been out with 50, 60, even 70-year-old men, who were not half as brilliant. And frankly, not necessarily even as mature.

Heck, Marcel Duchamp was 24 when he painted "Nude Descending a Staircase", a work that challenged the entire art establishment of its time, and is still to this day, a modernist classic.

"I have something for you," Ruff says, and my eyes blink with the gratitude of a damsel in distress being saved from a burning ship. "You definitely do," I think, internally heard and agreed upon by all of my cellular holy structures. He returns with a cookie. "That's for always looking so sweet," he says. I almost melt into the vinyl of my car seat, a blonde blue-eyed puddle of girl. "Oh Ruff," I coo. "Would you like some extra napkins?" he says as our eyes lock, and I watch him blush, watching me blush. "Umm I'll take whatever you've got," I quickly catch myself saying. He reaches out with them and our fingers touch in a sudden exchange of subtle chemical messengers.

"Oh! I think I forgot to leave an extra tip," I call out, just as I was about to pull away, possibly in search of an oxygen tank to stabilize myself. "Oh that's not necessary," he says, with the ever-open ever-giving energy he always seems to be steeped in. "I absolutely insist," handing over a crisp Lincoln, being more than the cost of the coffee itself. "I mean you're all so hard at work... you deserve to be appreciated," I assure him, willingly overplaying my hand of infatuation. "Well I always appreciate YOU Cybilline," he smiles back, and winks. OK, I've got to get out of here right now before I swing open that car door and ravish that young man and find out how soft his godly wavy hair follicles really are. I clumsily semi-speed off with a gentle wave back. But as I reach the road, I look at the coffee cup to take a sip and see a perfect pink heart has been scribbled upon it, with Cybilline written across the heart in black marker.

Sweet sugar of God.

SEQUENCE NINE

One reason Santa Fe is called "the City Different" is because of its architectural dissimilarity to other major travel circuit destinations, but also because strange stories abound about uncommon connections made here, unique callings, and definitely true individuated characters drawn to the energy of this high-altitude atmosphere, that lends itself so well to dreaming. On occasion, possibly hallucinating, but that's another book.

Some like to disparage it as "Santa Fake" because it's a city that was essentially constructed as a huge art project: consciously adopting the Southwest adobe look back in the 1920s as a mandate, largely at the behest of a New York City transplant architect John Gaw Meem, who provided the modified formalization of the original native style, a movement called the Pueblo Revival, which now, even the IHOP and Walmart today are forced to make their outer shells conform to. This, all in the name of maintaining a city aesthetic that separates it from all others, to drive what's been the central economic engine of this town for over a century: well-spent tourist dollars. Many buildings with just the surface veneer of adobe are called "fauxdobe" as a dig at the pretense. But the entirety of this city's flirtation with dress-up is really only fake if you don't believe in art. And I wouldn't worry about the opinions of such primitives as that.

Where truth is concerned, Santa Fe is indeed the oldest capital city in the U.S., founded over a century before the United States became a country. And these charming adobe structures evolved directly from the traditional Pueblo architecture and the Spanish missions in New Mexico, which allow residents today to live with a blissful awareness of ancient history mixed with the modernity of America's smallest international city. So there's nothing imaginary about that. Not that Santa Feans have ever minded imaginary. This has long been a city proudly built on a well-constructed sense of fantasia.

With the remarkable smooth texture that holds cool air in during the summer and warm air in during the winter, delicious radiant floors warming your toes, attractive nichos accentuating the walls, vigas across the ceilings, corner kiva fireplaces, and with gorgeous curves and rounded edges throughout, creating a sensuous sense of space, one wonders why the rest of the world hasn't better caught up to what we've already figured out in our architecture. Stop living in drab square boxes and improve the charm of your life immensely! Why not add a canale roof drain, for goodness' sake, and far better than a 'Home Sweet Home' sign, one could hang a delightful red chile ristra on the portal leading to your front door! Warmth, charm, tactility.

Doors are also a big deal here. Always wooden, often with geometric shapes carved into them, and commonly painted teal, these doors can be intersections to bathrooms, yards, or be connected to an outer wall leading into the property, and of course, serve as the stately carved entrance to your courtly humble dwelling. They can even be mysteriously free standing, reminiscent of the doors of your very mind, adding to the legend of portals across the state leading to other worlds. That sensibility existed here long before the most world-famous UFO encounter of the twentieth century occurred in Roswell, New Mexico, where news of the crash of a flying disc in 1947 made it into the morning paper headlines, before later being denied by authorities. There's even a museum there to commemorate the evidence, often intentionally comically, but not ever without true belief.

These doors may even have appealed to Jim Morrison, who claimed to have seen Hopi Indians laying dying from a car collision with a truck on a desert highway leading from Albuquerque to Santa Fe. Occurring when the singer was an impressionable five years old while living in the state, and when I-25 was still a dirt road. It was one of the defining moments in his life growing up, leaving such an imprint on him that he entertained the idea that some of those Indians' spirits may have entered his body on that morning. "The Doors of Perception" perhaps appealed to Morrison not only from Huxley's book, but somewhat reinforced by a lingering image of attractively mysterious doors that he had experienced seeing in his childhood.

The less mysterious doors I walk through now are those of Coyote Cafe, from whose tall windows I will also view this evening's radiant sunset reflected as a golden hue on the buildings across the street, as I have a date with two ladies tonight. One is a painter/sculptor in her 70s, born and bred Santa Fean, who creates floating motorized vulva to express the buoyant joys of female sexuality, and the other is a store owner in her 40s, my friend Ting-Ting, of an intriguing birth of Tibetan and Australian ancestry, who specializes in textiles. I met her a few years back at the Trash Fashion Show, where the guiding rule is that attire must be at least 75% recycled or reused materials, and she used the Tibetan love of bold color and pattern to great effect, with outrageous snow leopard toy accessories, and a painted petrified popcorn necklace to resemble yellow coral. This often hilarious runway experience is part of the Recycle Santa Fe Art Festival, which is something I attend religiously each fall. The idea that one man's garbage is another man's treasure has never been more apropos.

What excites me about tonight's dinner is that we are three generations of women with very different backgrounds on the surface, sharing the common thread of being united by internal sensibilities, with an adoration for the absurd and the sublime. It seems an obvious sensibility to carry, but it eludes so many! I am wearing a bracelet from Ting-Ting's shop of artist-made clothes, which has been the source of many of my best accessory finds. I'm looking splendid head to toe, combining the ridiculous and the classy, the kooky and the timeless, for a truly Santa Fe vision of the modern woman.

"Miss Cybilline Farroh!" Sunny says, arms outstretched. "We have your table all ready, right over here. You are getting the VIP table tonight," he winks. Sunny is the amazing GM at Coyote Cafe, my favorite restaurant in Santa Fe. It's got the best balance of supreme appetizers, entrees, cocktails, and desserts, where every aspect of the meal is as strong as the other. And that height is magnified by the entire service staff. The whole crew functions like a dance of the pixies, magically choreographed to avail at every turn, without the distractive din of bustle. They never interrupt or bother, and yet always seem aware of when someone needs something, and then swing by occasionally with some complimentary delight to indulge in. Sunny is my hero, always making a special space for me and my guests. I think of Coyote as my second kitchen though you'd have to be pretty well-to-do for that regularity of presence to ever be enacted.

"Great to see you, Cybilline," one of the bussers says as I walk by. "Always so beautiful," one of the waiters says, grabbing my hand. This is what celebrity must feel like, except that this is genuine, based on personal connection, and not on what someone wants from you, or hoping you'll take a selfie with them. Though the latter has happened!

Maria was fairly conservative she has said, in terms of belief in family, Jesus, and yes, an undying worship for the sanctity of grandma's recipes, until she neared 40. This highlights a natural divide that exists between those who grow up here and those who feel called to move here from afar, the latter of which lands far more spiritual than religious, and more emotionally independent and free spirited. But having gone through the Santa Fe public school system and pursuing the path of a dutiful wife, for Maria, something happened. She fell in love with a bad boy gringo. Her family didn't take well to it, but she was also freed by their rejection, because she was put in a position to choose between respecting her own deep feelings or her family's deeply held opinions. Recognizing the paths of possibility her life could have so easily taken, if not for the destructive awakener of love, her heart then cleared a path for a new Maria to step forward.

She began to question, "If those things I was raised with were simplifications and only partial truths, what ELSE might I have already made my mind up about that is also an unexplored doorway, blocking me from some great joy." The hypocrisy of limiting yet controlling beliefs had frustrated her into accepting her freedom.

"How did a nice Catholic girl like you end up creating these images," Ting-Ting says, scrolling through her phone at Maria's latest work, to be displayed at the Form & Concept Gallery later this month. "I mean, it's graphic yet tasteful still, but I know you've come a long way, baby!" She has a child's grin on her face, still not looking up from her phone.

"It's a statement about freeing your sensual expression, which for me was so curtailed the first half of my life. That floating flapping vulva is about having no shame anymore, and about the celebration of the body. Especially at an age when people are telling you not to celebrate it but to shut it down," she says with frank confidence in her mission. "I am saying invest in your pleasure, move forward in your bodily exploration at all ages. Because what I found, is it got better. That the age stigma was untrue."

"Oh I get it, loud and clear," I announce, raising my glass. "And I honor you." I look at her with pride. There is no level of vulgarity in her work, even though it would be so easy for it to be so. Her long history as an artist working in the strict traditions of producing Spanish Colonial art, brings a dignity and sophistication to the physicality of what her focus shifted to so many years ago, while still communicating a refreshing unbridled joy. Her Hispanic heritage and knowledge of techniques passed down for generations have served her extraordinarily well, for the time when her spirit was ready to really take flight. Her elevation is grounded in something solid.

"Something that's so interesting about you Maria, is that we all grow up with ideas about being young and then being older, what someone in their seventies is like," and she nods in agreement, while lathering the extraordinary corn-shaped cornbreads with honey butter that Coyote serves before the appetizers. "But you're the start of that new world, where seventy-year-olds are the hippies, the psychedelic revolutionaries, whores and weed connoisseurs who got naked out on the lawn. THAT's who grandma is today!"

She laughs and nods as she takes a bite. "Well also funny, because I was 19 in 1967 for the Summer of Love, and obviously that was going on around me in Santa Fe, which had plenty of hippie sensibility, with lots of celebrity presence moving here and making the news. So yes, I was in that generation, but it wasn't my world. My family and my circle of friends were still so innocent to all of that stuff. I've become that person now of course, but there's an irony there, at least in my mind. I was sheltered from it at the time."

"You were sheltered from your salvation," Ting-Ting says, holding up her phone, causing Maria's face to light up and blush, as she laughed. "That's one way to think of it," she chuckles.

"I can't believe I haven't met you before," Ting-Ting gushes, "because when Cybilline told me we were having dinner, I recalled seeing an article in the Santa Fe Reporter when I was just a kid, about the local woman who sculpted in the nude, which my parents were so mad at me for finding that." Maria laughs and squints her eyes in remembrance. "And that was you!" Ting-Ting continues, while reaching for her water. "But I've been doing the mother with a 15-year-old son things socially, so I guess that's why we haven't met... And what's weird is I'm in my early 40s, around the age you were in that article, and feel like I have less energy than either of you two do now, and don't seem to have the same interest in sex. I've dropped off!"

"What?!" Maria exclaims, eyes bulging. "Yeah, but you give me hope," Ting-Ting clarifies. She has a unique take on so many topics from an unusual variety of familial and social influences. Her grandparents, like other refugees of Tibet, were drawn to Santa Fe in the early 70s, with its 7,000-foot elevation and uncommonly high aspirations of spirituality, surrounded by desert terrain, snow-capped mountains, bright blue sky and adobe homes which, they said, "felt familiar" to Tibet. It's why even today you will see Tibetan prayer flags blowing in the breeze throughout the city, in a mutual embracement of the culture. But their eldest daughter met Clint, a strapping Australian hiker and photographer with a comforting but casual interest in Buddhism, and while they met and solidified their relationship in Santa Fe, Ting-Ting's mother, like Maria, broke with family traditions, and moved to Australia where they would have more freedom to pursue an unregulated life and grander financial prospects. They returned to Santa Fe however just a few years after Ting-Ting was born, to have more help and support with child rearing from the larger Tibetan network here. As always, be careful what you run away from.

Clint got into real estate to bring money in, and he worked hard to keep western sensibilities and interests on Ting-Ting's radar growing up. She continued the westernization by falling for Seb, a vacationing American she met Down Under after returning to Australia to experience college abroad, a fortuitous benefit of her Australian citizenship. Their meeting luckily coincided with the birth of Instant Messaging on this frontiering new phenomenon called the internet, where people living at far distances could now connect for hours, with Seb logging in right after work in California, which meant catching his new love just as she was starting her day in Sydney. This felt astoundingly romantic and yet cutting edge. From his desk at a tech startup, he shared his DIY music with her on a brand new social platform called MySpace, and yet within a year, found himself hovering madly into Her space, when she returned to the States to visit her parents for the holidays. Canyon Road famously has a Christmas Eve Walk, jam packed with people caroling, art-hopping, surrounded by candle-lit brown paper bags called farolitos, sprawling in every direction, and hot chocolate stands for sipping. He got caught up in the dance of the City Different.

Seb was as charmed and smitten by Santa Fe as he had already been by his new paramour, and manipulatively, perhaps —or just recognizing the power of an open door— he quickly hooked himself up with a job at *Outside Magazine* in Santa Fe's downtown Railyard as a marketing art director, and she soon said goodbye to her adventures in The Land Down Under. Seb had doubled the attraction of moving back home and of course her parents wildly approved of this whole situation. Even today a portion of Seb's salary goes toward funding Ting-Ting's clothing shop in the Baca district. Just 20 minutes from town, they live in Eldorado for the slight distance from her family it affords them, and for the good school system there.

"I think..." I start to interject to Ting-Ting, "that you have to be vigilant, with each passing decade that you tack on, that you don't become a rolling stone gathering moss." Maria immediately laughs.

"Ladies, here are your cocktails," Martine our waiter says, flanked by a runner who is carrying mine, a cute thing named Logan, who is always sure to make eye contact. "I'll be right back to take your order, but I want to tell you about a few specials tonight you might want to consider." The three of us are happily clinking glasses because we can already anticipate an incredible night here in my second kitchen, as we take in the array of options.

"I don't get it," Ting-Ting says to me. "What do you mean by a rolling stone gathering moss? It sounds... rather dirty, really." And she shakes her head like the Queen of England.

I laugh and think how happy I am to be introducing these two people because this is a perfect energy dynamic, which is the whole point of arranging social dinners. Figuring out the right ratios, like a good recipe, but with personalities. The melding of experiences and sensibilities into a pleasing mix is part of the meal, but even the meal itself is just a component of the true purpose of dining out: to be transported.

"I just mean we start to buy into numbers, convincing ourselves we are these roles we play, and psychologically aging ourselves into a box." Maria nods. "And if you don't listen to me," I tell her, "the next thing we know, you'll start cutting your hair to be 'age appropriate' and making conservative dress choices to avoid any hint of utilizing your feminine wiles," I joke, smiling, knowing this is one thing she's not capable of. Entertaining herself with outlandish adornment is how she and I became friends. "If I look in the mirror and I laugh, I know I did it right," she told me early in our acquaintance. It's the one true release Ting-Ting seems to have always left space for, to show up for herself, despite whatever other demands are pressing upon her.

"Like for me," Maria says with sudden solemnity, "that 40 wasn't the beginning of a downward slide, it was really truly the beginning." She maintains that gaze to Ting-Ting so that she feels it. "You ain't old, lady. Not even close."

"I appreciate you guys so much," she says. "In Asian philosophy, there is this idea about the process of becoming 'new' or becoming the child, so I really relate to this. I'm going to start meditating on that to invite it in. I've been giving too much attention to the child outside me, and maybe not enough to the inner one."

Sunny swings by with a napkin folded over his arm, and three tiny bowls on a platter. "Just wanted you ladies to try a little treat from the kitchen. This is our mushroom bisque," and places a tasting spoon down in front of each of us, followed by the soup. "You're the best," I say as he treats us to a small enjoyment, before our appetizers arrive. He winks as he leaves and all three of us girls moan a little upon first ingestion.

"Cybilline, that necklace!" Ting-Ting yelps. "Is that a miniature car in a teacup?!" and she laughs, putting her hands over her mouth.

"Jennie Cooley made this. She's got a studio in Eldorado!" Her mouth gapes. "Yes, I have to introduce you, I know," I say, seeing the name not registering in her eyes. "She'd be perfect for your shop! Everyone asks me about my necklaces everywhere I go and they're pretty much all from her."

"I'm really just starting to think about exactly how many people there are in town that I don't know," she says. "She's probably my next-door neighbor," and she shakes her head but in her way, displays no sign of frustration.

"Did she make it specifically to match your car?!" Maria asks, smiling as she adjusts the distance of her view that allows her eyes to focus on the details. "I saw it parked on the street when I was coming up Ortiz," and I nod affirmatively, pursing my lips after a quick refresh of moisture balm.

I'm still so in love with Esmerelda after all these years. Simply touching the steering wheel, without even driving, brings me joy. People often act like it's such a privilege, but it costs less than the average new car, all these bland Tylenol capsule vehicles. Truth is, people choose to pay for the practical convenience of trunk space and fuel efficiency, instead of for an experience of beauty and the delight of environment that classic design provides. I swear that old car keeps an extra spring in my step. She's kind of my friend, and often I protect her from the rigors of aging.

"That's a serious boy magnet," Ting-Ting concedes, which sounds funnier coming out of her mouth than Maria's. "It's from the 50s, right? I'd say, could attract young and old boys alike!" She winks.

"Funny you say that, I got that car in Nashville and the guy I was seeing there just loved to spend hours working on it. And watching him work on it was," and I stop speaking to finish a remaining bite of the cornbread, "...absolute foreplay."

"When you say seeing," Maria says, moving the little spoon back and forth as if pulling more information out of me with a string. "You've never been a one-man girl?" "Well, no, but I did go there because this god of a man, an incredible, sensuous Colombian I had met in New York City —I called him 'Thiago the Tiger'— went to be part of a graduate program in human development, and I decided to chase him there."

"He was there to teach? Or he was a student?" Maria says with an eyebrow raised, and we all laugh.

Just then, the Squash Blossoms with mascarpone, the bowl of Bacon Mac and Cheese with mild green chile, and the Venison Carpaccio, a dish made with huckleberry compote, cherry mostarda, pinon oil, crispy rosemary, pecorino, bitter greens, and crostini, arrive and we start divvying up the portions to share, and slow bite by slow bite, enjoy the revving of the engines before the entrees arrive.

"Well, I got a place by the Pancake Pantry in Hillsboro Village, then left Tennessee for Los Angeles a short while to seek new ground, and only went back to Nashville to see Tee give a Ted Talk after his studies, and fulfill his request for a smooch for graduating. But during that trip, I had a vivid dream about being in Santa Fe. It was so weird. So when I got back to LA, I drove up through Joshua Tree, figuring I'd check things out here for a week to just follow the muse and clear my head, and then, BAM! I never left."

"That is a version of a story you hear so much of in this city," Maria says emphatically. "Do you know how many people I know who were driving through on their way to someplace else and like, their car broke down here, and they never left. Or came for a visit with no intention to even consider staying, and couldn't bring themselves to leave, and created a new career just to stay, and end up doing something closer to their heart for a livelihood. It's like the city has a mind of its own and is a magnet for the people it's supposed to ensnare."

"My parents left and came back, then I left and came back," Ting-Ting adds.

"Land of Entrapment," Maria says. We all nod yes.

"Which is not such a crazy idea," Ting-Ting relates. "It's like the energy vortexes of chakras in your body. Why would it be surprising to find vortexes on the planet? These swirling centers of energy. They exist!"

Not just true of your body or certain locations, I would say it's true even in the paths we are drawn to in life, vortexes that pull us to one interest or another. Part of Thiago's life experience was recovery from the fight of addiction, and he could not have been at this dinner with us, drinking, for instance. He had to stay away from that and was grateful for having a new lease on life— but in that energy struggle, found his reasons to move forward, a calling in helping others do the same.

And we had a similar sense of mission, but for a different population, a different set of life lessons, different ways of being saved.

Art was where I felt that debt of gratitude. My first impression of incarnating on Earth was that this simply had to be some kind of mistake; a cosmic wrong turn on an interplanetary journey. But the discovery of fine art suggested a meaningful path forward, that could be believed in. It came and saved me from the prospect of a dreaded boredom, a life of Other People's Inventions, and the heartless story of mundane unenchanted reality. I knew if I was going to exist in this world, that it would be my place to nurture the flourishing of creativity in whatever population I was drawn to, as it's that aspect of the human experience that holds, I believe, the highest opportunity for evolutionary advancement of this species.

When you create in any artform, there's an aspect of the process that's like touching hands with the angels... The Dionysian exploratory play of creation can teach 'permission to the forbidden'; a regality principle related to finding joy and pleasure, and making things fun. That when you can't laugh about something, it means it has control over you. But in your regality, you know you are far larger than your circumstances. This permission to live elevated also helps extinguish the triviality of ontological guilt carried within your interstellar consciousness; that shame-based anxiety that's a remnant of primal ooze, as low-end a spiritual impulse to the soul as a 7-Eleven.

After all, you're not responsible for the way existence is structured. You don't have to apologize for what the universe is. Any more than you're responsible for fixing what someone else has broken. You're just here on the ride, which is a gift that some treat as a curse. For instance, I would never begrudge a strict plant-eater their pleasure, but often it's a choice made as a result of guilt, an expression of the great chain of sustenance being an unacceptable system to them, which they seek to correct. No matter how well meaning, playing God is its own prison. Telling nature what is permissible and how life 'should' be designed is like a cloud telling the sky which way the wind should blow. It's funny but whenever I think of how I'd orchestrate reality, I just think of how some of my good friends would structure existence based on their preferences... and I know for a fact I definitely wouldn't want to live in their world. So there's a strange justice to not getting things all our way. It evens out, and gives everyone an equal opportunity to be disappointed.

I meanwhile honor the regality of vegetation by not denying that we know plants feel, including a caterpillar walking upon their leaves. They can sense changes to their environment, including the tone of people speaking to them, and have nervous system responses to music that they grow towards in pleasure or away from in vibrational retreat. They are conscious, communicating with surrounding foliage using roots under the soil, even sending out warning signals. And there are over 600 species of carnivorous plants that specifically capture and digest prey, including the non-stationary plants like the free-floating Waterwheel.

Then there's the Drosera Capensis which shows clear signs of consciousness as it wraps around its prey like a snake. They are such remarkably complex feeling, sentient organisms, and to limit their reach, as it were, to simply being seen as the most convenient food source for humans is truly to ignore vegetative agency entirely.

Facing the fact of having to eat other living entities, that prefer not to perish, so that we may survive, brings a unique philosophical tension to the surface, which is better taken on than ignored. Because walking through that door leads to illuminations on other great mysteries of existence, including even the nature of the universe itself. Is our cosmos this dark sadistic uncaring cruel beast that destroys all it encounters under an insatiable appetite? Or is there, once again, a secret royalty theme hidden in the dynamics of this mysterious reality, containing threads of higher purpose, of a redemptive glory beyond the facade of life's brutal chaos?

The first thing to note is that the human idea of justice circles around whether 'bad' things happen to us, or if 'good' things happen that we like. If there's bad weather for our big event, then it's unfair, because rain is after all the great ruiner of plans, hairstyles, and moods! And if we get sunny weather, then good fortune has smiled upon us. But maybe the soil and the plants needed that rain as a great day of nurturance and replenishment. Many things are good for the cycles of existence, but not for humans. Death is a great example: we just don't like it. And if humans could have things their way, our great species-wide dream is to live forever! But would that be a just world, when in doing so, we would not be leaving room for future generations to occupy the limited territory and resources available, and to have their own opportunities to explore this life? Clearly the cosmic justice of our being structured to perish is an ultimate good, and not at all a sign of the universe's darkness. It's just at odds with human justice.

Perhaps, as some others believe, the cosmos is really indifferent in its nature. That it's all just time happening, no more invested in life's stories than the ticking hand of a watch.

Or is the nature of the universe punitive? One funny idea that was promoted to question eating meat was that you were ingesting the fear of the animal and it was bad for your spiritual system. But I watch public television, so I wasn't fooled. Every nature documentary I've ever seen shows animals always running for their dear lives from some great predator. Is the lion being tricked into eating its prey's fear, because the universe is an asshole? Or likewise, the old idea of sin as a basis for human experience; that's also taking a punitive stance on the nature of being. That we should hold a dread or guilt over the facts of existence, requiring redemption by some foreign hand to save us.

We need to evolve these ideas, which is done first by challenging them. Cracking open their shells and probing their contents.

For instance, I would argue that something you might describe as 'loving' is at the core of our own process of becoming, in how we follow our 'joy' to guide us to knowing what's in our hearts, to learn who we are. What an interesting way for that process of self-knowledge to function! I couldn't help but notice it. Could the universe itself be loving? In how it provides a multitude of opportunities to get it right. That the fact that matter has the ability to communicate (It doesn't have to!) is a sign of a universe that gives its inhabitant creatures a chance, a leg up. Even though the world is feeding off itself in a lustful festival of self-ingest bordering on horror, I think about this beautiful tension: how every day, we take one step closer to our death, yet as we grow every day, we are also born just a little bit more. There is a give and take, a retracting and releasing that is symbiotic, behind the scenes of the natural world and its psychodynamics.

In a way, the small world of insects is a colossal key to understanding the big picture of how it's all connected. First and foremost, insects are animals, made of muscle, which is meat. And Exhibit A is found on our very own flesh. There are mites, which are animals that live all over our skin, our face and eyelashes. We simply don't see them— and these tiny arachnids, like insects, share in so many of our animal traits, including the desperate flight from pain. Being microscopic doesn't mean their sensations are microscopic to them. Just as our studies of fruit flies have shown they even experience residual pain shortly after some injuries have healed.

You can't talk to them and ask these things. But look at the incredibly ornate detail among insects, whose small size tends to make us delegitimize their tactile realities, believing they are little automated machines that don't experience any sensations. Such depth of care having been placed by nature into constructing their appearance and function, must give us pause! Consider the Portia Jumping Spider. We would want to believe they are somehow stupid because they have little brains, yet these almost imperceptibly portioned spiders, one fifth of an inch in size, show astounding strategies and mental acuity that proves thought processing is not about brain size. And how inspiring, the intelligence and color and intricate structure that can be seen in those details of this spider's physical beauty and capacity!

All evidence that the universe is far more vast than just our perceptible world. And you don't have to go into space to see how vast!

The same rules apply going smaller to bigger. If you've ever seen big cats playing, meaning lions, tigers, panthers, they play just like your house cat. They rub faces, play tails, jump and pounce for fun; your housecat being far smaller in comparison does not affect their likeness of being in the least. Whether big lion or little domestic kitty, all cats have the same number, shape, and arrangement of teeth.

Even the itsy bitsy world of mites still have males and females, with penises and wombs. You do the calculation. But know this: We wipe these animals out of existence every time we bathe, and that is by design. It's really an intoxicatingly beautiful transmutational story of the victory of eternal life, the king's crown itself, as demonstrated by endless energy cycles feeding off each other and renewing.

So yes, the painful destruction in that energy transfer between sentient life forms is real, but the magnitude also varies by which lens you look through. Entire planets and ecosystems are constantly destroyed and then reconfigured into new forms throughout millions of galaxies. Imagine even the emotional pain from the sheer volume of broken hearts that scream out as entire solar systems explode, leaving only space bubbles that in time become new worlds. It's a true fact. But the permutations of consciousness just live on.

We have to say yes to all of it. Perhaps you can hear the "Not Guilty!" verdict in the higher courts of interplanetary existence? Where you are permitted the timeless throne, and sitting upon it, a lesson in worthiness. An acceptance that allows light to enter and shine out of you. Just like the lion, who never questions his birthright to being proud and regal. It's why we call a group of lions a pride! Sure, he will go down one day, but he'll be zestful and without shame at what he is or his place in existence, until just that last moment of breath.

The delightful hot flaming and sultry filet mignon with pecan, espresso and anise rub, comes to the table, alongside Maria's Elk Tenderloin and Ting-Ting's favorite Crispy Branzino.

"I have to take a picture of this, the presentation of the elk is so remarkable," Maria says, angling for the right light.

The fetching busser Logan slinks by and gives me a wink. "Is it to your liking?" he asks with a steamy glint in his eyes, which I accept. "I should say so," I tease back, without having taken a single bite, as he well knows. "Well I'll be back to check on you," he says with intent, before handling the long-neck water pitcher for the table to our left.

Ting-Ting grabs my hand after he's passed by, and leans in with a gushing whisper, "He's like Joseph Gordon-Levitt in Mysterious Skin!" She laughs with amazement. "Can we all just acknowledge how many men, from 20 to 70, are hot for Cybilline?" while Maria just looks at me, with her 'yes, girl!' face on. Ting-Ting looks back over at the young man now serving the opposite side of the restaurant, performing his attentiveness, and she gawks playfully, "How do you do that?"

"Isn't the issue, why are people worried about it," I ask, as I start to play with my food. "We're probably all about 12,000 years old, give or take," I say with a whimsical smile. "We're certainly not the ages we appear in these skin suits."

"There's your answer," Maria tells her, sipping the water now with a squint, and adding, "I certainly had more than one life in just this one."

"I have a client who tells me stories about growing up under his father's rules, and it's so clear to me that he was an older soul at 7 than his father was at 40, and that they incarnated specifically to explore those dynamics, where the father by all appearances was the figure of experience and knowledge in Earthly terms, but where the son understood things practically from birth that were wiser and more expansive than his father would ever know. Like many artists, he was scarily precocious from the start and his threatened father would scold, 'Don't go above your raising!' to keep his young brilliance in check. But that poor man pushing back against this challenge to his ego was probably 50 lifetimes behind his son."

"I'm not making a fuss about it," Ting-Ting begins to clarify. "It just seems these days it doesn't even matter if the two people are having a relationship or not, there's a weird, shallow condemnation for different aged bodies intermingling. It's a specific hate speech reserved just for ageism."

"That's their limitation," Maria says, "no reason to borrow it. But the most obvious flaw in the logic against it, let me tell you, is the crazy notion that there's an equal power dynamic based on proximity of how many years you've lived." Maria shakes her head. "Nonsense!"

"Right," I add, quick to agree. "There are power differences in every level of relationship dynamics: If there's a wealthy man and a poorer woman, that's an unequal distribution of power. Even if one partner is super attractive, they may exert a greatly uneven influence for what they want. And an older person may have more experience, which is a type of advantage, but maybe the younger person has more physical strength, more know-how, or just has higher intelligence. And maybe both people gain from each other's advantages. But most importantly, exploring those dynamics can also just be a hot and stimulating pursuit, and a healthy one at that."

Going from free love of the sixties to nudist spouse-swapping of the seventies, it certainly is a strange place to find ourselves, if there is any advancement at all, that post-sexual revolution decades have landed us in a social demand for compulsory monogamy or this recent fragility at age differences. My dear friend James Broughton, a poet and avant-garde filmmaker, was 62 when he met the love of his life, Joel, who was 26. Talk about a numerology figure eight! People can wear shocked expressions all they want, but those two lovebirds stayed together almost 25 years until James' death. What more proof do you need of love's triumph, and that it doesn't function in neat encasement, painted always inside the lines. I never met anyone with a more successful passionate creative romance, so what are all these dictates people attach themselves to? What false god does it serve?

"People are wired differently," Ting-Ting slowly intones. "Like I really work through intimate connection. That is how I emotionally understand things. And you love to be independent and yet make friends in ways I, who supposedly loves relationship to others, could never do. You can chat up anyone, and understand interconnection better than I do, and I know that. But I couldn't live like you and you couldn't live like me. And those different perspectives are part of the strength of our friendship."

While the story of the Tower of Babel relates to how we all speak different languages across the planet, and so have trouble understanding each other, I find it just as interesting to see that from the positive spin, in how our differences exist in support of nature's divine diversification.

Let us speak of the koalas of Australia. Did you know that they eat almost entirely just one thing, which is eucalyptus leaves? Which by the way, have almost no nutritional value. And that almost all other living creatures would find eucalyptus leaves to be toxic and even extremely poisonous. So there's a whole niche of the ecosystem that nothing else ingests but basically this one mammal, and it's essentially the only thing that creature devours. Likewise, there's an Aussie marsupial, the numbat, whose entire diet consists of termites, and no other insect. These examples are eloquent peepholes into seeing how specific the needs and provisions of the ecosystem are, that this marsupial's existence is predicated on maintaining that termite population. Everything is so perfectly provided for. It's so very exact and ordered, and not at all emblematic, or a hallmark of, a random universe. It's quite remarkably organized, to the last detail.

I've always let my knowledge of these creatures teach me why people may hate the very things I love and adore. Of course we don't like those eucalyptus leaves! They would make us sick. But the koala's love for them is of the utmost importance. The Law of Abundance demands diversity of taste. Otherwise everyone would be on line for the same resources. So just think, it's good when people hate what you love. Bless their displeasure.

This is also why we can love people for having qualities we don't necessarily like about them; once you see how those characteristics support the aspects of their personality you really appreciate.

"How is everything?" Martine says, walking by. "Up to expectation? I just saw your face," he says to Maria.

"Holy shit," Maria exhales, "this elk is... oh my god. So soft." Her eyebrows raise like those in attendance of the famous unwrapping of King Tut's embalmed mummy, when shocked archeologists witnessed the fully erect cock of the 19-year-old king, with each onlooker exclaiming in some disbelief, "How Can It BE?!" Maria loves the drama of ingestion.

"I think I'm ready for another drink, Martine," I say, which he knew because he was already taking my glass off the table. "The one with the lychee, lime, and Empress Gin?" "I will have that right for you Cybilline," he says, and looks at Ting-Ting. "I'm good for now," she says.

"The vegetables have such a great compliment to the flavor of the meat in this dish," Maria says, "I feel like that should happen more often. One thing you can say for Mexican food is it does blend the legume, the grain, the vegetation, the meat, in a cohesion. And Coyote is not Mexican, but it's blending the ingredients at that scale, and mmmm," she moans.

"What do you say Maria," I ask point blank, looking at her plate, "do you sense consciousness in all that vegetation?"

"You bet I do," she says. "Yes. You smoke marijuana and what are you going to call that? You are merging with the plant's consciousness, and I'd say getting smarter from it." She lifts her fork like a finger. "Maybe plants have an older intelligence." She chews and squints.

"And all those witchy spells, made of herbs, don't get me started," she adds with gumption. Her black eyes are radiant, and I love watching her chew because she takes such pleasure from it. "Do I have to mention how earthly life unfolded from eating from the Tree of Knowledge? What kind of plant is THAT?"

"And isn't that a funny idea," I remark with a slightly inquisitive face. "We're talking about a guiding philosophical principle that espouses there was something WRONG with tasting from the tree of knowledge. Whether of good and evil, or any other form of knowledge. As though saying YES to the journey of consciousness would be a sin!" I almost yell, as my drink is placed in my hand by Martine, and I wink.

Ting-Ting looks over in realization of such a startling foundational principle, "Yeah, that's messed up!" "What god," Maria asks, "would wish any creature, much less his creation, to miss out on that journey, to not learn about everything under the sun? That is why we're here," she concludes with her patented deer-in-the-headlights yet firmly aware expression. "To enjoy things including pain and not knowing."

"I just want to point out," Ting-Ting quickly interrupts, "Buddhism is a religion without a god... We didn't need one." Maria looks at her and nods pensively. "I like it," she says. "Though for my criticisms, I do believe in God. But not a vengeful god, or an insecure god, but one who wants you to know your power."

"That's an interesting way to say that, Maria," I say, "that's what we do, isn't it. We learn our power..."

"I believe that is the reason for so much shame placed on the body, on sex, coming from religion," she ruminates. "At a time of course, it related to no birth control options. But I think it's more insidious than that. It's a matter of not feeling the reverberant energy of your flesh, because that's attached to feeling powerful. Your sexuality can strengthen you and make you believe in your own sensations. The body can liberate the mind. And if your body is a dirty thing and you inhabit a sinful vessel, then you don't know that force of believing yourself to be powerful. You are dirt. So even though the kingdom of heaven is within you, you should be less than that, and reach the kingdom instead through the church, because you cannot be trusted, you of dirty body and mind. Ha!

No thank you..." She touches her finger to her temple and then up to the sky. "But the big lie I saw past was that there is no terrible ego in feeling elevated and powerful. It's just adult to feel that way."

And I cut the last of my steak. Taking a bite, it might as well be sinful.

I would never claim to be Mother Teresa, but I could probably tell you a number of things she wouldn't. It's not just religion where that shame exists, but across the sea, repression doesn't have the same hold. For instance, there are sex drive-ins in Netherlands, Germany, and Switzerland, so you can pull up and do it in your car. With sexual activity being an inevitable aspect of the human animal, they don't bother denying it or to shame it, and instead endeavor to make it safer and not so hidden. Granted, prostitution was legal in the United States at the start of the twentieth century, but nowadays you couldn't even put a scene like a sex drive-in on an American television show, even though it's an example of real everyday life, because healthy sensuality, like body image, is not a priority here.

And really, why would any aware adult get conned out of the opportunity to take care of their urges for $50 and be done with it? Because we're holding ourselves for marriage? I can assure you, something like a male escort service would thrive and bring much joy in this town so highly populated with mature single sophisticated women! But you know, if we're raised since early awareness with rules of virginal decency, to believe that's shocking and corrupt, then we may never question our implanted instincts. This is why it's important to find a good sex therapist if you've built up a relationship to your body shroud in shame and taboo.

I think the same shame felt in notions of pleasure, for many, even extends into their dietary choices. If we consider the link between food and fornication, the guilt-based proclamations of Catholicism in not enjoying the flesh for its own pure gratification, are mirrored in the vegetarian approach to eating, which limits the radical sensuality of cuisine in favor of adherence to imposed moral restriction; limiting the pleasures of refreshment to being solely for acquiring nutrients, only for function, and not permissible for the intoxication of the senses. There also seems to be that same religious pious feeling behind it, often paired with a kind of 'being saved' language adopted by its initiates, who likewise seek converts to the 'new path' they have found. And holy shame! upon all others. Could there be a less appetizing thought than replacing all our chefs with clergy men?

Granted, I would love to hold industry accountable to maintaining regulatory standards of humane treatment for animals. Quality of life, while you live it, matters. If you think it's of no consequence what pain and circumstances are suffered because they're going to die anyway, just apply that logic to your own life and you'll quickly see the folly in it.

"If it were ever revealed, the depths of misrepresentation across the world in every philosophy, just to keep people sedated," Ting-Ting says, shaking her head in thought. "We live in such times of deception."

"I don't mean to be ignorant," Maria says, "but is there also that body shame in Tibetan thought? I guess I'm thinking of how the monks refuse sex."

"There's a belief that the flesh is Earthly," Ting-Ting concedes, "and that just for the monastic population, that monks separate themselves from worldly life to the degree they do, so they can open their hearts so deeply without distraction, and be a conduit for bringing that unfiltered light into the world, through meditation. But remember, Tibetan Buddhism is fully into tantric sex, and marriage is purely secular, so it's a different sensibility."

"I think I need some books on that tantric business," Maria replies. "It's never too late." She reaches for her black clutch handbag, pulling out her phone, and I'm almost expecting her to place an order for the Kama Sutra right there and then, but instead lifts it high and, quickly corralling us, says "OK everyone, lean in," as she snaps our obligatory photo. Then sneakily I see her take a quick selfie of herself performing an exaggerated wink. "That's for Parker," she confirms coyly. It's funny how many people are annoyed by the supposed vanity of selfies. Women have been making themselves up in front of a mirror since the dawn of civilization, and if you think the idea of that hasn't always been that there was some inner camera there taking pictures of each angle, in every step of the makeup process... then I guess you don't know much about girls.

Martine swings by, and holding up a long rectangular menu asks, "Are we ready for dessert?" "Are we ever!" I exclaim, pulling the menu and angling it back toward him so he can read as I point. "Yes!" Maria shouts. "We'll take this, this, and this," I say, indicating my selections for the table, a choice entrusted to me. "I'm almost done, don't take it yet," Maria says to the runner trying to clear the table of her last bites of elk. He removes my and Ting-Ting's plates. They provide new napkins for all three of us.

"But Ting-Ting, you were talking about it being times of deception," Maria continues, as she carefully scrapes the fork against the remaining bits on her plate. "Don't we always cover everything up. Think, why WAS it such a big deal that I would create my work in the nude, and that people had to feel scandalized by it. We have laws against walking out in the world in our natural state. That is a bizarre perversion of your right to be what you are, isn't it? Your own natural naked body?"

"And yet I'm only partially bummed about it," I tease. I mean, I may not think people should be in restaurants naked, but Maria brings up such a glaring example of the degree to which we demand an artificial construction of our environments to be comfortable, the need to be placated with a falsity. Which I say with full appreciation for the civilizing effect of garments.

"But when Seb and I went to Amsterdam, people were in the park naked and no one even looked over. It's legal there and just wasn't a big deal. But we in the Land of the Free make it a big deal. We are a highly programmed culture," Ting-Ting remarks.

This is true, there are so many programs, it can be tricky to unravel! A friend from Nashville told me how she used to drive their family truck at age 13 with a grocery list from her mother, including smokes and drink; a journey taken every Saturday morning by herself. And I thought how intriguing it was that we've self-regulated our everyday lives to remove many simple freedoms, as though the opportunity of liberty is too great a challenge for us to handle. The age of consent in America has climbed to 18, which is the time in life we're already going to college, while in Japan it's 13. And in Italy, Brazil, and Germany, it's 14. Iceland and France, 15. My goodness, life expectancy during the Roman Empire was only 25. When do you suppose it's OK to start living? At the age of 10, Orson Welles was sent by his parents to travel Europe alone to learn self-reliance. Turns out, the current idea of wearing training wheels into adulthood isn't protecting our youth, but crippling them.

It's no wonder why American college students, who in a sense were not respected enough to be handed the dignity of being trusted with agency throughout their teens, which builds critical self-confidence in the maturation process, now need 'protection' from ideas, to the degree that they have demanded 'trigger warnings' to feel 'safe' before being 'exposed' to uncomfortable topics, which every generation that preceded them handled without squirm. Free speech isn't there to protect the ideas you already agree with, after all.

It is education's purpose to expose us to difficult material and handle divergent views. Yet the fragility shown by students trying to prevent ideas they don't like from even being expressed, has in many cases been supported by the colleges whose social function is to produce adult minds capable of navigating thorny realms of human thought, in preparation for dealing with daunting challenges. But they've been failed by those institutions who have given them permission to instead put their heads in the sand where they feel safe. Yet if you've been told "You can't handle yourself, you're a child" until you reach college age, then we should not be surprised when the infantilization succeeds in a kind of cultural backslide. Even asking to be shielded from ideas represents a disintegration of the integrity of the human psyche. Not exactly a sign of evolution.

"Wouldn't it be interesting if we returned to the old American ideal of when people just thought you should do what you want, and say what you want?" Maria asks rhetorically. "It's the only way to be realistic about human nature."

"Too much freedom," I tease, "not enough control." People today pick up their cellphones the way they used to pick up a cigarette, to transfer social anxiety and personal tension onto an object. It's an existential uneasiness we carry, and we feel more in control by taking action upon a thing. Albeit placating, it's not always a good instinct.

"It *is* about control, isn't it?" Ting-Ting says. "That's the source of so much moral outrage."

Maria quickly catches a busser's attention by softly but subtly shaking the empty water glass to indicate she needs it refreshed, and then lifts her cocktail toward her mouth, with eyes full of mischievous thought. "I'm guilty of giving in to the attempt to control," Ting-Ting continues to ponder. "Like this eastern sensibility I wanted to believe in, that all actions need to be nurturant. Well, being with Seb," she continues, "he definitely fucked that belief out of me, that everything had to be about nurturance."

Maria spits her cocktail back into the glass. "No, I mean it's good to be a little dirty," she clarifies. Maria laughs louder.

"My point, I guess, is there needs to be balance," Ting-Ting patiently asserts. "Most of what I know of Tibetan practice is from talking to my grandmother and it's an important way we bond. But truthfully, I believe the world isn't grappling with eastern and western sensibilities as a way to balance each other. There is the eastern non-attachment approach that some take as the path, of not wanting, and the western indulgent way, less discipline and embracing chaos, almost with too much wanting! And my conclusion, out of respect for both, is neither is right, neither is sufficiently complete. I love the east for its detachment and love the west for its irreverent passion. And I believe you can find an enlightenment in the middle, like the way Jodorowsky's film 'El Topo' is so profound." "Yes," I sing out in praise, "one of the greatest films ever made."

"He uses so much eastern thought within his western violence," she enthuses. "And it doesn't seem radical to me to recognize that eastern female yin isn't the answer and western male yang isn't the answer. The path is a balance of both, and is specific to the temperament of every person."

"With some couples," I relate, "the woman has more yang and the man more yin, she more commanding, he more pliant. And that can shift depending on the topic. The balance doesn't just follow physical lines."

The desserts arrive, and Sunny is carrying another small plate, as Martine and my breathtaking hottie Logan start placing our dishes at the center of the table. "This is just a palate cleanse," Sunny says. "We made a marzipan ice cream today, and also this green basil sorbet. Let me know what you think."

I.   Think.   I'm.   In.   A.   Culinary.
Brothel.

As Sunny departs, Logan leans in close with a smile and says, "I know you're gonna enjoy that." He really has magnetism. I grab my utensils in preparation for battle, as the hand-to-hand melee begins.

Forks and spoons start crossing over false boundaries into exotic realms of mystery and exploration. As the evening encroaches on revelry, each clinking of cocktail glasses somehow take on the mystic energetics of tingsha bells, after which I believe Ting-Ting was named. And with We Three Queens at this table, connecting the knowledge of three generations, Kingdoms will fall.

"What are you thinking?" Maria says, interrupting my thoughts of removing Logan's shirt as I take my first bite of the Banana Cream Pie, which is the best I've tasted. "I guess I'm thinking how primitive our civilization is," I reply, even as I just then place what can only be explained as an experimental interaction with the flavor profile of marzipan into a far superior version of itself in this chilly form.

"I recently learned," I begin to explain, "that Anais Nin had a husband on the East Coast and another on the West Coast, who never did find out about each other until separate obituaries told variant stories," I tell them. "And I thought, why IS it that we can only marry one person. Who says?"

"Men have been bigamists forever," Maria says matter-of-factly, "but if a woman dare enter that realm, you know she's in trouble. And that it couldn't be love, it's that she's a tramp."

"Well," I say, now tapping on the burnt flesh of the crème brûlée and cracking it, "the more I thought about it, the more I believe this is actually a highly contemporary arrangement. That in the future, this will be more of a sensible and convenient norm. And not a scandal."

"Well wait," Ting-Ting interjects, "this is cultural." She hesitates only to move the spoon from the green basil sorbet into her mouth. "My mother's half-sister remained in Tibet and had two husbands, who were brothers from a neighboring village that co-married her. It's called fraternal polyandry." She nods her head affirmatively as we all sip from our drinks. "Men and women there don't actually find the sexual aspect of sharing a spouse unusual or distasteful... No," she says, seeing us both raising our eyebrows, "that's where common jealousy is different in a culture when detachment is prized more." There is a certain hush, as we all seem to sip at the same time, and where you can hear the busboys' shoes walking by across the carpet, as we wait for who will follow that up. I can't stop my smile from coming through. "Well you may laugh," Ting-Ting shrugs, "but she had greater financial support having two husbands combining income to raise a family with. It's that practical."

I keep laughing into my hand and Maria and Ting-Ting start laughing just from the contagion, saying "What?" "Whaaat?!"

"I wasn't laughing at that," I say, "I'm just thinking how many traumatized couples there are where one partner cheated with their brother and created generational scandal for their families, this black mark... of broken hearts, shattered lives, and deep feelings of betrayal and devastation... when they could've just moved in together!" Ting-Ting reaches for my glass and takes a sip of my cocktail.

"They could have shared bodies, and reaped the benefit of shared income while they're at it," I say, tapping my head. "Of course!"

"Just like sharing this drink," she says to me, with a shrug, taking another sip. "That's really good, I'm going to get one next time." Having surely ingested enough gin already, she makes the approval smirk of a baller. "But point being, there are lots of valid ways to make your arrangements with intimate partners," Ting-Ting reiterates.

"If two consenting adults, or three or four, can have fun, passion, romance," Maria says, "what exactly is the judgment?"

"It's supposed to be a free country," I say. "But everyone has forgotten the main principle of maintaining that: Mind your own business."

"Ha! I think social media unfortunately robbed us of that," Ting-Ting says, as she also cracks the surface of the crème brûlée. "Everyone thinks they need an opinion on everyone else. They just get up in each other's faces."

"Oh, they always get in your face, since long before social media. It's like me and Parker, we still have mmmmmmm," Maria says with profound vocalization, taking another sip of The Gentleman's Vice, a Bourbon Manhattan cocktail smoked with cherry wood in a decanter before serving, "such a strong physicality together. But back then, age difference wasn't the scapegoat for people's intimacy neurosis. It was the mixing of races! That one's OK now," she raises her eyebrows high, "but we caught hell for it." She finds her spoon's way into the bread pudding and dips it in.

Ting-Ting takes aim at the other end of the bread pudding dish and our spoons hit as we both go for the same piece. She playfully clinks the spoon to mine in an act of utensil fencing, or a bit of tipsy cheers.

"Oh Cybilline, we need more of this!" Maria says laughing. "Girls' night out!"

After we've paid the check, Sunny stops over with three glasses and places them on the table. "I just want to make sure you leave happy," he says, and we blush as he pours the complimentary Montenegro, a digestif crafted from a blend of 40 botanicals. He keeps a measured facial expression, careful to pour evenly, just a touch into each chalice.

We clink glasses for one final round, that medieval sign of auspicious life, and hold them in the air like the ringing of a bell. "That one's for you, Sunny," I say. "Thank you for taking such care of us."

"Cybilline," he says with a pause, "you always leave just a little dessert on the corner of your plate." He looks at me with slight ponderment.

"Oh, I leave that last bite for the angels."

SEQUENCE TEN

There is a knock at the door and I pull back the patterned Turkish curtains from the window. It's my neighbor Joss, who only moved into the small furnished attached studio next door a few months ago, but there was an instant recognition at first glance; a new friend who felt like an old friend. He even got an extra ticket to the Fleet Foxes concert at Santa Fe Opera and offered it to me, which utterly surprised and delighted me.

As the door flings open, he steps in immediately as if already in mid-stride, saying "I'm so excited to see this show!" He holds up the tickets like he's won the lottery, and hands me my ration.

The Santa Fe Opera is no small fête. It's visited by 85,000 people every year from around the globe, a world-class outdoor venue which the Wall Street Journal has called "the Rolls-Royce of American summer opera" with our sprawling stunning sunsets as its backdrop. And when rock shows are performed here, it's even better. Add to that, Fleet Foxes' video for "The Shrine / An Argument" is as close to a Crosby Stills & Nash experience as contemporary music gets, and with their haunting harmonies blending with the colors of the sky, what's a girl to do but say yes?

"The pre-show tailgate parties at the Opera are legendary," he says, as I quickly slip the ticket under a refrigerator magnet for proud display. And that's true, the Opera tailgate is practically local heritage. But it's not a barbeque and hot dog kind of tailgate, it's a high-class Santa Fe version where people dress elaborately, daringly, and set up ornamental tablecloths with lavish meals featuring fine wines, finger foods, cheeses and truffles, turning the parking lot into a charming social event of mini-opulence.

"And check this out, I've been dying to show you this shit too." Joss starts scrolling through images on his phone of young guys getting fingers-deep into rugs. It's called tufting. It sounds like a new sex act, but it's just a new frontier of home nesting.

"I was thinking tufting is like a distant cousin to the upcycling you do, using all the string and fabrics," he suggests. "Well," I say looking at the images, "they're cousins that I'm not sure even speak," as I smirk at the screen. "And some of it..." he scrolls again to a large-scale Mae West tufted wall hanging with background elements inspired by Basquiat, "isn't embarrassingly bad." I laugh. "Are those our only standards? Yeah, her tufting game is strong. I can see the upcycle connection." In fact, little does he know that one of my first upcycling projects involved tearing up a shag rug made of woven fabric fragments and re-applying them to my ensembles. Tufting in reverse. But I will leave that for a later reveal.

Making himself at home, he takes the coffee pot and starts pouring himself some morning fire, Santa Fe's own roast of Black Lightning by local fair trade bean roaster Aroma. He explains to me, as he puts the pot back down, that tufting is a movement and it will make men softer, more comfortable doing inner things, and not just outer things. Men used to be raised to be the master of outdoor activities, like mowing the lawn, hunting, playing sports, and women did all the inside tasks, like sewing and cooking and decorating. I don't seem to be entirely breaking the mold on those stereotypes myself, but I just nod in acknowledgement as he says, "This is a long arc of change in deeply instilled identity structures that we are living through right now."

I both share and don't share his enthusiasm, because I remember bra burning. I mean, jello was once served exclusively to members of the Royal family... Now it's served exclusively to hospital patients and political detainees. Times change! Like all social attitudes, views on gender roles live on a continuum, where some aspects of cultural gains remain, while often surprising ones fall away and become lost. After the long strides made to be taken seriously, young equality-minded ladies today will fully support a woman getting up on a stage in next to nothing, writhing around and moaning some crap, as nothing but a backdrop of tits and ass to some not particularly impressive dude, and they fully accept her purely objectified role, and have no issue with her complete abrogation of quality and substance. Would the man singing ever accept such placement in the production? Certainly not. And I don't mind playing sex kitten, of course. But all I have to do is ask myself if I would agree to perform that role behind some guy on stage, and of course the answer is a very clear definitive no. Unless the guy was Robert Plant, because then the squirming moans would be real.

"I mean, gender expression is a funny thing," he continues. "It took Joan Jett to finally put a set of balls on Crimson and Clover." Of course, I am a fan of the original Tommy James version too, but he isn't wrong.

He opens the box of Whoo's Donuts on my counter to help himself to the White Chocolate Lemon Pistachio one that I wanted. "You're splitting that in half, right?" I say. He cuts it in two as I ask without breaking stride, "So, you're a musician," taking a bite of the curved confection that has long entranced me. I don't like to admit it, but Whoo's was the first place I ever went in Santa Fe. It was somewhat of a test. Because a town without a good donut will be a town without a Cybilline. "I've heard a bit of you working on sounds through the window," I tell him, "when I was gardening."

"Oh yeah," he leans forward, grabbing a napkin to put under his donut. Tidiness points half-scored. "Umm, well I came here from Austin, playing conventional alternative stuff, because even 'alternative' of course is standardized by its own set of parameters. Mostly guitars and black jeans." Chews and says, "Coventry, Ohio originally." Seeing me looking up attentively with my coffee in hand, he finally sits down. "But I've really started branching out into exploration since getting to Santa Fe. Which isn't necessarily what I expected... but I feel more set free of the rules here."

And I think I know what he means. I used to dream that I lived in this house that had other rooms I was aware of, but didn't have a way to access, that I couldn't grow into. And since moving to Santa Fe, I never have that dream anymore. Because somehow being here finally gave me access to those spaces, adding dimensions to my life and to my identity. I'm tempted to say it added two or three additional rooms to the house of myself. It's hard to put in words, but it's a great sense of inward expansion.

Joss had tried to join the rock music scene in Austin, but found out as a gay man, playing in beer-drenched bars and with gender norms not being nearly as fluid as we may be led to believe by news headlines and tufting trends, that there are still no songs on the radio of a man singing about his love of another man. Just over fifty years ago it was illegal to hold another man's hand in public, much less kiss, in all fifty states. Homosexuality was defined as a mental disorder by the American Psychiatric Association until 1973. Even with the legalization of gay marriage, I will repeat: there are still today no charting songs sung romantically from one man to another. So how accepted and integrated in culture are our same-sex attractions and enactments really?

In particular, he expresses a disgust for all the beer drinking that was part of every music venue in Austin. "You can smell that shit on people," he says, taking another sip of coffee. "When I get a whiff of strong alcohol on someone, it feels like self-medication, like they are avoiding something in themselves. I don't know…" he searches to identify it. "Escaping reality, maybe. I just don't like it."

This is an interesting take because I see TV watching, video games, magazine culture, and khaki pants as an escape from reality. Most of popular culture appears to be a distorter, a form of imprinting a false normal that directs the traffic of your neurotransmitters to accept banality as a golden standard on one hand, and on the other, a litany of medical and crime dramas suggesting murder schemes and surgical tragedies are as commonplace to our everyday lives as standing in line for coffee and donuts. The messages we receive are not informing reality, but distorting it radically. I decide not to go that route.

"But…" I clear my throat, "I seem to recall from some of the things I've smelled out in that yard, that you like to get high a great deal. Is your weed smoking running away from life?" He looks at me like that's silly. "I'm not sure beer has ever given anyone insight into their existence, but weed and psychedelics are a different matter."

"Shakespeare, Hemingway, and Bukowski would disagree with you," I challenge, but add, "Granted, beer is not my chosen steed."

I pour a little honey and half a teaspoon of coconut oil in my coffee, with just two taps of cinnamon before stirring, as a substitute for milk and sugar, thinking about this topic of getting high and its potential benefits to creativity. "I would say anything that can get you past the confines of the prefrontal cortex, into the flow of less literal and dream-like states of mind, and untangling of your inhibitions has potential value to a person's growth and personal awareness." Here is probably a prime example of where the therapeutic approach and worldview in dealing with artists may differ from the more square-box ideologies of accepted pedestrian logic on the topic of wellness, which is usually patently riskless.

I lean towards being a proponent of lubrication. The substantial messages of social control around us —in particularly the assault by capitalism's refiguring of reality in its own image; that of self as consumer— is itself like a mind-altering drug. As a counter to this, substances can be used with awareness, to turn on to life and tap into perceptual stirrings within us that are often covered up and encased by our usual waking defenses. Defenses which are magnified by the information overload of modernity. So if you use lubrication for sex, you can use lubrication for creativity. And certainly the greatest rock stars have been elevated to the status of shamans with a little help from the hooch, and I consider them soldiers of a very real war in culture. Why would any form of soldier be expected to be free of requisite dangers? It comes with the territory.

Joss munches on the donut with surprising care in giving a good long chew before swallowing. "I try really hard to remember that we all receive our signals from different sources," he says. "And I appreciate Bukowski enough to amend my prejudices. Gotta admit that... though I will not start drinking beer."

His sweet face is a front door to an equally amiable disposition, and I pry further into his process. I ask how he navigated the blockade that the challenging bar culture presented to his art. It is, after all, what we do with what we are handed that makes all the difference.

"Well, I decided not fitting in was probably my thing, not a problem but an answer. So I went to a noise-sound panel trying to go more fringe," he says, "where I realized the two most interesting things happening there were the snoring of the guy to my left and the jackhammer from the construction across the street to my right. So it turns out I'm probably right of real fringe, but still left of alternative."

He's entertaining. Everyone should have a gay neighbor. I'm intrigued that he feels an outsider in both the music and gay scenes. "There were these hot men with long hair," he says, "that actually cut their locks to normalize and conform to a gay uniform: short hair, tight t-shirts, requisite muscled body, brand-conscious wardrobe to form a manufactured sense of All American Boy, which itself is missing the point, the opportunity of being different. And that kind of self-packaging of normality to fit in, to be acceptable, I saw happened a lot, to where it was another scene I just had to abandon. I can't get into any situation where that many people want to erase their oddness to be part of the crowd. Unless," he says, "you're in drag, where you're free to be eccentrically expressive. Because it's just a performance. That's not dating. For that, it's back to the short hair and tight tee uniform."

I smile at his confidence. "You want another of these? The other one is Lavender Blueberry Blue Corn," I say, already cutting it in half. "Oh yeah," he reaches for it. "Santa Fe is surprising, right? So many yummy things. So many." He shakes his head in pleasure, then continues the theme. "It's funny because my folks were very accepting of my coming out, but my father actually said I should expect a lonely life." He makes a face. "That's interesting for him to project that onto you," I reply with curiosity. "But then maybe he knew you wouldn't fit in?" "Yeah, but that would be true if I were into girls too," he says in half-chew. "I haven't been disappointed in my options." He shrugs and wipes his mouth with the napkin. "I just get so annoyed when my parents think things about me that are so untrue."

"Yeah... but are you going to stop believing all the little things you think about *them*?" I query.

"Oh hell no!" he replies, almost bursting into a laugh. "But I'm right about all those things." "Oh... OK," I giggle, taking another bite.

Meanwhile, his job seems to have provided him with whatever the gay community hadn't. "Got that job within six days of arriving," he tells me, raising the coffee cup in the air as some kind of flag wave of success. "Immediate family." He scratches his head and starts pulling on his long shoulder length black hair in a slight petting motion.

Joss works at Meow Wolf's exhibition space and even though he doesn't have much traffic with their art teams while interacting with the guests at the front desk, he says it's a perfect balance of good pay for low stress work. And they provide lots of snacks, which allows for a semi-party-like atmosphere. Lots of music shows, too, which gives him ideas of how he could go forward with his sonic explorations.

"What's cool with these people... and why it's maybe the coolest job ever, is the whole alternative reality, portals to strange worlds, you know? And after living on the outside of all these confining social roles that everyone seemed to accept... the big houses, with lawns, and square jobs for square people— who were going to raise square families, and live lives of paying bills and social climbing, but with no real risk of adventure to the soul."

And as he speaks, I sip my coffee and squint a little, because his words are like a recitation of many of the thoughts I had when deciding to pursue the role I've played with my own life.

"And what every young person being bred for that factory existence of modern society wants to know is," he says, this time raising his finger, "that you can escape that. That your life instead will be a free one."

"Well, Joss, it sounds like you really landed in the butter," I say. "You came here without a place or a job, no guarantees, and got yourself settled in 10 days. Santa Fe is known to either accept you or spit you out, and it showed no hesitation with you, my friend."

"Yeah, I was embraced, I have things to learn here," he says, "I can see that. You want more coffee?" he offers, as he starts to pour himself a splash more. I laugh at his continued ease with me, "No I'm good. I've gotta get ready, I have clients today. But why don't you get brunch with me on Saturday at Dolina?"

"Oh yeah, I want to go back there," he says, "You know that hot waiter that looks like Joe Dallesandro?"

I nod that I may vaguely have noticed. He shakes his head yes with an eyebrow raised, to indicate his interest in that.

"I have a feeling you'll help yourself," I say, mostly to myself.

After he's left and gone next door, I think how lucky I am to have such a budding connection in my direct surroundings like this. Could it be a little gift from guardian angels to have, without intentional planning, a sense of discovered family right in my midst.

The two living room walls are adjacent to each other and quite independently, Cybilline and Joss place their hands against the wall facing the other, feeling the space and pressing against the warm texture of the adobe, unknowingly mirroring each other. Both send an energy of warmth and appreciation across the divide, with eyes closed.

If there had been no wall, their hands would've touched palm to palm. They will never know they shared that moment.

SEQUENCE ELEVEN

I could never start getting dressed in the morning and honestly think "there's just nothing to wear" because what lay in the enchanted realm of my closet is a treat for the senses. After all, I made my personal incision into almost every garment in there, like a signature. But I could, and often do, think there's nothing *new* enough to wear. Nothing virginal enough, untouched by the residue of previous experiences. And today I'm taking Angus for a long ride, so I'm making an extra effort to add a dash of vim to my accoutrement.

Peeking at the clock, I have approximately ninety minutes before I need to pick him up. Brainstorm, oh how the mind races! I look to the ceiling where so many ideas are stored for download into receptive minds. I thrust open the cabinet doors of my armoire, of which I have a few. It's a very important element of decor in Santa Fe, not just for the look provided by distressed paint and hand-carved reclaimed wood, but because adobe homes often don't have closets, a subtle ode to a world before sewing machines. Lucky girl that I am, I have one in the bedroom that I've removed the doors on, to help exhibit like a gallery of paintings, the color and texture displayed within. But prized still are my decorative armoires, this one with cholla wood for handles. I can especially appreciate that with these rustic charmers, all the little cracks, discoloration, slightly uneven planks, minor scratches, and other age-related imperfections are considered enhancements.

Grabbing needle and thread, I carefully pull open a drawer holding so many overflowing fabric ephemera of scraps, bits, patches, snippets, yarns, and embroidered appliques of the fine fiber arts. Queen Cybilline is taking measure of her royal subjects! There are always a few more items in need of renovation and elevation. Eyeing textiles and placing them by instinct for their energetic resonance, I cut, pin, sew, and knot-tie. Witches make brews based on all kinds of powdered and herbal elements, from dragon scale buds to frog toe. They stir the cauldron, and in cartoons, cackling all the while. I however take an alternate tact to the alchemy of shapeshifting, here in silk.

And it IS magic! One difference between a world of garments and no garments is that fashion allows you the wild opportunity to be seen as no one has ever witnessed you before— a color, a pattern, an aura you carry that is totally unique to the moment. No matter how many days that exact physical form of yours has inhabited the earth, it hasn't done so wearing THIS. So I feel resplendent walking into the world in a blouse and pant ensemble that didn't exist even an hour ago! Angus will sense something special, not from what is seen, but because the way we experience one another will have been sweetened simply by the subtle pleasure I exude in unveiling my new creation. I spin before the mirror and curtsy to the spirits.

Having retrieved my alluring passenger, we drive up into the Sangre de Cristo Mountains down Bishops Lodge Road, just about ten minutes from town, to begin our adventure with brunch at Auberge Landmark Kitchen. They have the best breakfast cocktails, including the Western Repose, a Reposado Tequila drink with pistachio, amaretto, and orange peel. There are so many ravens artfully flying about the well-maintained property, almost performing the aesthetics of northern New Mexico, that you'd believe they were on payroll. Everything is delicious, with coffee served in ceramic mugs made by an extraordinary local potter that goes by the moniker of *Whiskey & Clay*. The weightiness of the mug and its unique glazing makes the drink it surrounds and contains feel more exalted, a potion.

While brunch can't be hurried, we must be sure to finish up before two o'clock to realize my plan of taking a tour of the Windows of the Earth cave. This is a follow up to the Ra Paulette movie we enjoyed so much last month. As I researched, I discovered one of Ra's caves is located steps from a hacienda style resort called Origin at Rancho de San Juan. Taking a trip to see it in person has my heart racing and Angus is possibly more excited, because his own work involves architectural elements for his installations.

I had wanted to take the High Road to Taos route, so we could visit another site on the way, but after the languid service at Auberge, there wasn't the time. It would have added an ingredient of quiet reverence to have walked through the National Historic Landmark known as El Santuario de Chimayo, where a small sample of Holy Dirt can be removed from the prayer vestibule and purchased. I envisioned having it in a satchel against my leg when riding horses this evening. Darn the languidity! But then again... that's what other days are for, isn't it?

  RADIO REPORT: — "MYSTIC" BY GALACTIC WITCHCRAFT— PLAYS AS WE DRIVE NORTH ON US HIGHWAY 285.

Santa Fe has so many historical churches, including the oldest in the country, San Miguel Archángel, built in 1610. But there is something uniquely special about El Santuario de Chimayo, located 27 miles north of Santa Fe, where worshippers walk in an annual pilgrimage during Easter Week, with some 60,000 people trekking as far as 90 miles by foot (to my mind, an astounding thought!) all the way from Albuquerque. Granted, I find the journey just as religious by car, with the views of the drive breathtaking and divinely infused.

But as houses of worship go, my own secret pleasure award goes to that tiny private church that sits up on a hill by the side of the road, called the Cerro Gordo Chapel, near Canyon Road. Surrounded by barbed wire and built just from local boulders, it could only hold about four people even if you could get inside. Barely a structure, it manages to still have "The dead depart, their works remain" inscribed upon it in Spanish. Always with an eye to the sensibilities of the artist, is Santa Fe! But I have a prediction that Ra Paulette's Windows of the Earth is about to take the throne in my mind for Places to Honor Energy.

The resort offers a $25 public tour. The first 30 minutes of which is talk from a guide on the special cryptobiotic properties present in the soil of the area, and characteristics of local flora and foliage. Then an hour walking carefully up and back to the site, including just a little over 20 minutes in the cave itself, which is plenty for the opportunity of marveling provided.

It is an inexpensive tour but a pricier resort, and those staying can be very wealthy, which in turn can mean impatience when immediate gratification is not being offered. The introductory discussion about the composition of local topography was worthwhile and clearly relevant to the full experience being shared, but a couple of young ladies were probably more interested in tanning on the deck of the resort's balcony than hiking up to a handmade cave, and they couldn't help but distract as they entertained each other. Of course, there are people who are bored no matter what miraculousness may surround them; having money doesn't buy you eyes to see with or the good sense to appreciate.

There is this subset of the uber wealthy leisure class, whose lifestyle in its entire detachment from the needs of survival, leans toward the illusory, and can seem its own kind of divine justice when observed at a particular angle. There is a tedium, after all, in their mysteriously cultureless existence that comes through in each unriveting tone of their speech patterns. Perplexing to have that much wealth, that much access, and so little clue about what to do with it. And people don't believe you when you say you needn't be jealous of them, that you have all that you need and far more in your humbler existence. As Andy Warhol liked to remark, the rich and the poor all drink the same Coca Cola.

I've counseled wealthy couples who seem to have it all. Of course I had to meet them in their home, lest they be bothered by the admittedly atrocious demands of road traffic in Los Angeles. But I've been especially glad of the opportunity for all I was able to see in these situations. The maids, the butlers, the calm household with abundant views, and little handcrafted lights peering up through the floorboards, conveying a riveting display of comfort and intimacy. But I also learned they had to hire a poor young artist to come by every Monday morning at 11 am for an hour to help instruct them how to perceive what lay just outside their own windows, and explain to them how to feel the effect of the visuals they'd installed in their estate. There was no live wire in their sensibilities and spirit, to be in alignment with the riches they possessed. I couldn't help think that, like insects in the ecosystem, their role seemed to be to keep the money in banks flowing, and to be the giver of resources to those seeking manual labor, like a tree supplying a hearth to its many living inhabitants. A critically important social role, but one in which they did not exactly play the part of King and Queen, despite a presumed lofty positioning.

Their love life, a mirror of the staid, placid calm of their largely silent home, but for the droning of that TV. Perfect temperature inside, even with windows wide open. But was there any heat in the bedroom, or even the flame of touch on the shoulder during morning coffee? Everything lived as if in a magazine, unruffled, unfondled. A very large bed, big enough to never cross paths in it.

Meanwhile "the help" was a middle aged latin couple who had small private quarters on the property, so that they'd be nearby at a moment's call. They danced in the evenings, left roses for one another, fed each other bits of food directly to the mouth, and had bountiful energy and buttery soft skin, with ample body parts built for pleasure; they rolled in bliss for hours each night, and shared a love for laughter and tenderness.

Who among these couples had the real wealth, beyond the illusion of material facts. Yet whatever may be obvious to the discerning eye, with humans untutored tendencies running amok, there is always a churning need for surface justice, petty disgruntledness, to convince ourselves the world isn't fair and create thick lines delineating the good guys and the bad guys, the have and have nots. Never imagining that their astounding shallowness of perception has blinded them to the maya, of who is in private hells and private heavens. Always sure that the lottery ticket of wealth should be theirs and would solve their griefs. But I assure you it would not solve their grievances; they would find those sources of unhappiness, and need for imagined vindications, somewhere in the lines of whatever life story would unfold before them. Because happy is too much burden.

Angus has been monk-like in his observance of the details of this hand carved space. He mirrors the motions with his hand, as if writing a letter in the air, using a language of ornate hand gesturing to communicate an appreciation for beauty. He looks over at me speaking in silent vernacular through his eyes. This is something you see more in artists than art appreciators: brotherhood. With the spirit of fellow creators, not just the works they produce.

One thing that makes these caves stand out in the modern world is the lack of convenience. There in nothing easy about them— there is no template to apply, no external coordinates to set in advance, and no aid from the genie in the bottle availed by computers. I look up at the light streaming down from the inlay windows, that serve the function of luminance as it's intended in the building of churches, cathedrals. Not light for practical use but for awe and contemplation. A coaxing out of the inner flame.

And no real money to be made in constructing it. This is a laborer's wage, that meets the daily need for provisions but nothing sustaining beyond that. The payment, as it were, is in the doing. I tell you, rare is the artist today so aware that process itself is the primary purpose of creating, as both a meditation and a way of learning the coordinates of the true self. As well as to simply fascinate and challenge one's own mind. But in truth, fun is reason enough, is it not?

"Come here," he says, outstretching his arm to hold me in it. "The mirrors are genius, to suggest water, as the clouds from outside shift the light in the space." This too like a cathedral; that impulse to dually experience a unique environment, that only we two shall share in our lives. Any future visit will only recall the first, that we've imprinted here. That emotional immortality of the fleeting.

Stepping outside for air, the uneven texture of the ground against your boots demands as much of your attention as the huge blue sky overhead, and the amazement at the large oval windows in the sandstone butte of the castle, reminiscent of the caves of the Anasazi, another of New Mexico's most treasured destinations, at Bandelier. There, you can climb into the alcoves, dwellings carved inside the mountain walls, where humans settled nestled within over 11,000 years ago, twice further back in time than even Ancient Egypt.

Ra's artful caves being far more domestic and secure from the intrusion of natural elements like storms or even mountain lions. For Ra, after all, despite his relative primitivism, still applies doors to his dwellings, with the modern convenience of the securities provided by a locksmith.

I've also planned a sunset horseback ride, and we have to get to the stables a half hour prior to the group embarkment on the trails. Wanting to quickly stop at the Lavender Farm on the way, we hit the road for the drive over to Ghost Ranch, where Georgia O'Keeffe made Abiquiu's unique landscapes famous. To ride on those historic grounds, itself an honor.

RADIO REPORT: — "ONLY YOU" BY YAZ— PLAYS DRIVING TOWARDS GHOST RANCH.

You generally don't have to wear headgear in the Southwest for horseback riding, but the dangers are truly few on this trek. The terrain is so flat, and so visible, there is nothing that can spook the horse, no surprise visitors from a wrong step of the hoof, nor snakes waiting under rocks commonly spread far apart.

Unless of course they were to encounter a ghost. The mountains here have all the feeling of ancient history in them, with their deep red and orange hues, containing thin white lines that indicate where, 220 million years ago, the land was under water that is now desert. For its modern incarnation, it was called Ghost Ranch long before O'Keeffe bought her place on a modest portion of the property there, just a house and seven acres of the sprawling 21,000-acre ranch.

Though O'Keeffe did live in Santa Fe at the end of her life, where she remained til the ripe age of 99, her time here in Abiquiu is the legendary stuff of true independence and art adventuring. By the time Georgia enters the Ranch's story in the late 1930s, this land had quite a history already. A paleontologist discovered more than a thousand fossilized skeletons of Coelophysis, a small breed of dinosaur, on the ranch property from 200 million years ago, a discovery made in 1947, the same year as the UFO event in Roswell. Then more recently, a mere ten thousand years ago, there were Paleo Indian cultures living there. When Spanish settlers gained the land in the late 1800s, they engaged a practice of stealing cattle and hiding them in the box canyon. To help with this scheme, they spread a rumor that the land was haunted and it came to be known as "el rancho de los brujos" — the ranch of the witches. Eventually the ranch was lost in a simple poker game, and the new owner adjusted the name to its current moniker. Still, the Ghost Ranch logo was adapted from a skull drawing O'Keeffe had given the owner during the charm of her initial visits.

Sometimes it seems like history is this separate, impersonal force— but it is not impersonal, it is created out of people's lives and choices every day. I remember as part of my art and psychology focus as a student, I was reading "The Secret Life of Salvador Dali" for school as a study regarding the life of artists, and as I laid it down to go to sleep, I wrote in my journal "OH SALVADOR... Make Me the Goddess of Your Floating Space!" in gushing youthful dreamy enthusiasm. And when I picked up the autobiography the next day to continue reading my adored Salvador's ramblings, I reached the passage where he called his wife Gala 'the goddess of my floating space' and of course, I was awestruck. While I don't think this indicated that I was Gala in a previous life, it was one of my lessons that consciousness is connected across time, and active; meaning history isn't trapped in the past. It's available now. And so is the future.

I have another kitty story to further illustrate. The brilliant Siamese cat Babette I mentioned, needed a feline friend. I knew that because I had a dream of a cat with a thick black stripe on its back being in our apartment, and instead of hissing or chasing, Babette ran over to her and laid on the floor, outstretching her arms to the right, and then playfully doing the same again, laying across the floor to the left, showing no aggression to this new cat, but inviting her with unthreatening non-territorial body language. I woke up and, taking that sign as a directive, contacted the person I got Babette from. She had the daughter of a very striking male cat I had met during my last visit, and

I agreed to take her, sight unseen. I only saw her eyes and face in the cat carrier when I went to collect her, and when I brought her home and opened her cage, Babette ran over to her and performed the exact ritual that occurred in my dream, with neither cat hissing, and Babette welcoming her, laying playfully at first to the right, and then the left. And it was at that moment that I noticed the thick dark black stripe —which is a highly unusual trait for an Oriental Shorthair— on my new feline's back, exactly as I had noticed it in the dream. I can't say this cat had "contacted me" that she was ready to join us through this dream, but it seemed ordained, and a factual instance of where I did pre-envision the playing out of an exact future occurrence.

This of course brings up the very old conflict of free will versus fate, in saying that if you're fated to do something, you must not have free will. But clearly they do operate side by side, because I could have responded to the dream by not buying a cat, but instead chose to believe in my vision. So major human spoiler alert: this is a philosophical dynamic our duality-wired frontal lobes simply can't understand, in that the human mind can't grasp the paradox of free will versus fate because two opposites can't simultaneously be true. By OUR logic. Just as we can't solve the chicken or the egg; that the big bang started a universe that somehow was nothingness and then became somethingness. But from where? It's not that it doesn't make sense, it's that our brains are not wired to be able to understand it. It's illogical. To us. Or otherwise expressed, it's a software that our hardware can't operate. Our brain after all is wired to the cycles of nature that it is made to operate within. It's not structured to comprehend ultimate reality, because we're not that evolved of an entity to have developmentally earned such a capacity.

The horses are all out in the paddock upon arrival, and I'm quite surprised to see other riders just wearing sneakers. I immediately pick up on the notion that we probably won't be trotting and galloping across the land, and sure enough it's a walk-only tour. Angus reaches his hand toward a black gelding with a white dot just slightly leftward leaning on its forehead, and an attractively saddled boy with a fantastic dark mane walks right over to me, and directly into my arms. "I think you get to ride that one," the trail guide says. "Name is Bishop. He doesn't much like other horses but he likes certain people." All twelve of the horses for the trail ride are boys, and I have no complaint with all that male energy. But there's a hell of a lot of anterior direction peeing going on before we get very far at all. The stable manager figures out I'm a bit more experienced than the others, and assigns me as Deputy Wrangler to bring up the rear and be positioned to yell at the horses trying to grab extra treats along the path.

It's a 90-minute trail ride with a brief break for appreciating the painterly sunset, where the guide dismounts and takes photos of each group with the wash of colors in the background. It really is the most beautiful land anywhere in New Mexico. And with two guides, one in front and one in the middle, they are able to impart a good deal of chatter on the history of the property while bringing awareness to where O'Keefe would have painted. "Horses are like huge psychic cats," the center guide calls out at one point, and I think it's a great description of their ability toward empathy and reading emotions. It's why horses are so successful in facilitating human healing through equine-assisted therapy, from making deep connective bonds with kids dealing with autism to soldiers with PTSD, to people struggling with addiction.

Even with a dozen people, the ride is mostly a meditative affair, where your main counterpart of communicative signals is with the four-legged body moving under your saddle. Angus turns around to playfully snap some photos of me from his phone, but the sheer force of the surrounding aesthetics demands the bulk of your awe and attention. I continually establish a bond with Bishop by leaning forward and lifting his mane to release the buildup of heat that collects along a horse's neckline, and gently scratching his withers at the tip of the saddle to put him at ease. He twists his neck often to look back at me, and appreciates when I dig my nails just under the harness crown, scratching behind his ears.

Showing him some attention, while being clear on what I expect, made it a delightful ride, just like with real men. Bishop touchingly rested his head against me after I dismounted.

With slightly stiff legs by the time we returned to the corral, I had wisely planned curative restoration with a jaunt over to the hot springs known as Ojo Caliente, meaning 'hot eye' for the circular pools you can bask in while dreaming away your physical cares. I've mapped out the day and night to just the degree Angus is finally picking up on.

"Where to now?" he asks, rolling down the window. He reaches into the backseat and grabs water out of his bag, as Esmerelda crackles down the bumpy path toward the main road, with Ojo less than an hour away.

"Give me some of that juice," I say, eyeing the water. "Earth juice," he replies with a grin. I touch my knee and push on a sore spot. After taking a sip from the bottle, I tap it and say, "This is a pretty good clue to where we're going next." He picks up on the suggestion immediately and lets out a hoot. "I was hoping, I was hoping," he double states. "From day one, Cybilline, you've been a geisha guide." He smiles out at the open sky. I glance over at him and watch his abundance. "You should have a local concierge service," he tells me, "you have a natural flair for providing direction to all the good stuff." Moving from my knee to pinching his, he grabs my hand, wedging his fingers in between mine and clasping, while sneaking his thumb in toward my palm for a gentle rub.

Scrolling with his free right hand, he stops on a photo from those he took during the trail ride. "I love this outfit, look how pretty you look," he says holding the phone for me to see.

"Oh god, I made this thing just this morning, before I picked you up," I finally admit. "Just for me?" he asks, leaning a little forward. "No, not just for you," I smirk, "at least not entirely for you. For the day, for pretty things to exist..." I list for instance.

  RADIO REPORT — "You're My Favorite Waste of Time" by Marshall Crenshaw— plays on the car radio.

He kisses my hand and emits an "mmmm" which is quickly routed in the senses to an associated form of craving, "I think we're gonna need food before we soak, no?" he suggests. "We shall indeed," I reassure him, while almost summoning my favorite sangria in my mind. They make a perfect blend, and don't think I haven't wrestled the secret recipe from them, but I won't share it. Of course, in theory, you shouldn't drink alcohol before entering the steamy douse of natural springs, but that would be insufficiently Dionysian, so I've pre-planned to ignore this guidance.

I place both hands back on the steering wheel, turning up NM-455 and Angus leans languorously against the door, peering over at me. After a time, he reaches forward to give a soft caress to my right hand, not exactly to help me steer. As the light shining through the windshield and illuminating the cabin is fading, it highlights the shape of his arm, with its ornate tattoos, which spread from wrist to shoulder, and sprawl all over his body. Watching me examine the work on his arms instead of the road, he lays back in the seat again.

"You don't have any," he states of my lack of tattoos. "No interest?" I shake my head. "It's very permanent, and I like my skin," I say. "I mean I love your tattoos; you almost wouldn't be you without them," I admit. "I wouldn't be," he says, "they are part of experiences that have made their mark on me. Even the creative choices in determining what goes where... it's a personal process that's self-defining." He looks out the window and quickly back at me. "If you did, what would you get?"

I purse my lips and squint. "It's very permanent," I repeat. The better I've gotten at living in the moment, I find it only increases my appreciation for the temporary and ephemeral nature of things. A sense of the transitory that is part of the magic of being, and the sheer plentitude of moments. Even with upcycling, things come undone, and you may re-stitch or change them up or reapply to a different piece, keeping even familiar ensembles in a flow of change. Just as wildflowers pop up in different places each Spring. The arrangement varies but the effect of their presence persists. All variants on a theme of everlasting flow.

"It IS permanent," he stresses with a shrug, "but there's room for plenty more permanent where that came from." He raises his eyebrows to remind me he knows all about making space for more, and then a little more again. I don't mention how he's paralleling my thoughts on an adjacent frequency. I just look over and say, "Cheers to that," as I turn into the long driveway of the resort.

The mineral baths at Ojo Caliente have been a gathering place and source of healing for thousands of years, and in fact, this site was the first formal spa ever built on a natural hot spring in the country, opened way back in 1868. These waters, rich in lithia, iron, soda, and permissible levels of arsenic, promise to aid digestion, boost the immune system, improve your mood, ease arthritic tensions, and most importantly, alter your consciousness until your gamma brain waves have calmed and soothed every nerve. Getting in those pools is like a subtle and natural drug. The touting of the healing powers of nature often doesn't really register for city folk, but these sulfur-free hot springs, ranging between 80 and 109 degrees, were an early tip off to me that I would be staying in New Mexico for the long haul.

After gobbling down the fare at the excellent farm-fresh Artesian Restaurant on site, we rush barefoot, much in contrast to the slow movement of all our surroundings, toward our destination. Customarily you don't speak while soaking in these ameliorative waters. You close your eyes and connect, quietly. You let your body and the water converse in the submersive language of mermaidic seventh heaven. Even so, Angus —a merman of sorts— has no trouble communicating with non-verbal expressions, and we hop between the five pools, each with their own properties impacting different aspects of the somatic system.

Above the mountain ridge cliffs overlooking the resort is the kind of night sky they only draw in children's books. A galaxy of stars across a pitch-black canvas. The silence in the air, and light hush of wind, a lullaby. A hawk flies overhead and above the sound of gushing water, I can hear each fold of her impressive wingspan as she passes, as if something is breathing directly into my eardrum.

Now some people will of course tell you this is bougie AF, and you should just go to the many free hot springs all around the wilds of New Mexico, which do stink horribly of sulfur. But I am happy to pay for the filtration systems that remove the horrifying smells of nature from Ojo's soaking experience, and am thrilled that others prefer the uncultivated setting found elsewhere. All the more room for our blissful relaxation.

Meanwhile, I have an incredible hot stone massage booked for first thing in the morning before heading back to Santa Fe, so I feel I've made the right choice for my preferences. Angus laughs hysterically in enjoyment at my lack of interest in the quaint impulse to over-worship nature, as among nature's aspects are the source of all disease and the haphazard murderer of life, as it eliminates us all to make room for the next incarnation waiting in the wings. Every medication you take is a scientific attempt to fight what nature is trying to do to you. No, I prefer art, which is a construct, an artifice, godly. Following suit, Angus likewise books a private massage for himself.

Ants, I am telling him, are much stronger than human beings, able to withstand pressures of up to 5000 times their weight. Probably gifted so because they are much more important to the ecosystem than humans are. But this is such an important point in understanding the cosmos, because while we may be stewards of this planet, there are levels at which we don't matter much.

As we sit on the wooden stumps that surround the small bonfires situated between the soaking area and the onsite hotel, I recognize a woman quietly strolling by. A perfect example of the opposite of nature that somehow has a stronger nature. She was part of this morning's tour at Ra's cave, and she had caught my attention because she is so dramatically makeupped that a part of me instantly loved her for it. Because, in her case, it feels like she reveals a truer part of her nature than nature would ever be capable of. Her painted features are as much salt of the earth as the simple unadorned women of Paul Gaugin's Tahiti years, recounted so worshipfully in his journal *Noa Noa*. There is such force in her performance of presentation; a kind of raw honesty amid the layers of covering up. I slyly nudge Angus to notice her. "From this morning's tour," I whisper, looking back over at her. He remembers, he says with his eyes. "She's amazing," I whisper. I am feeling grateful for her form of grace in this moment and look up at the stars overhead to send thanks, though no doubt it's partly the infused euphoria from the waters talking.

Further sangrias are ingested, and a perfect day comes to a close, replete with the sound of crickets. The flowing currents of this land have settled into our nervous systems, instilling a glowing feeling of ease, where all is right. I am exhausted yet elated, with a sense of heavenly rewards that seems to have permeated this whole summer.

If a moment could be a tarot card, this would be the Ten of Pentacles. And I am ascendant.

SEQUENCE TWELVE

In the morning, we have a soak both before and after our massages, and run into some of Angus' friends from Meow Wolf. It's a perfect opportunity for him to stay a bit longer, while I slip away to get back to town, and I encourage him to do so. Driving from Ojo, I am reminded of the exhilarating joy of not existing in a city. The sight of the mountains passing outside my open car windows, while still encountering the pleasant aftershocks of vibrations felt from massages by both hand and water caresses, makes me feel I really did something right in life to be living out this dream. And it IS a dream.

  RADIO REPORT: — "HOLY GHOST" BY TRAVIS BRETZER— PLAYS.

Without any need to rush, I decide to take a soft detour to Black Mesa Winery outside of Taos through a side road, where I can pick up some of their award-winning chocolate wine. Called "Black Beauty", you can smell that hint of dark chocolate while your tongue distinctly tastes a deep red Zinfandel, and your nose and mouth try to figure out what's going on. It's a pleasantly mystifying sensation and I'll grab a couple of bottles for home after sampling a few other selections in their tasting room.

Nearing Santa Fe a little past noon, I feel encouraged to further take the scenic route back toward the plaza, instead of continuing along the highway. Traversing through Tesuque up that winding Bishops Lodge Road, I dart around a turn after passing a slow poke, and to my great surprise, there's a cop standing in the middle of the street, with his hands on his hips, reminiscent of the archetypal comic book pose of a superhero. He outstretches his right arm in a straight line to indicate STOP. I don't even see a police cycle, and he seems to have come out from behind the bushes, so my first instinct is that this is some kind of joker in costume and I should be ready to speed away when he pulls out a hatchet, if my nerves were not calmed just knowing I'm in the relative safety bubble of Santa Fe, New Mexico.

The feeling of questioning reality is then magnified by his stature, as he's quite literally between 6 ½ feet tall to almost 7. He takes off his brown tinted sunglasses, and walks over to the passenger side, so that he's not in the way of potential oncoming traffic. I can catch the motorcycle wheel now in sight behind the tree, and his manor doubly assures me he's actually a policeman after all. As he bends to the window, I see a red pyramidic shape tattoo peeking from the very top of his buttoned shirt. A real policeman who no doubt plays electric guitar in his spare moments. Burnt auburn hair can also be seen coming through the edges of his black motorcycle helmet.

"I don't think I WAS speeding, officer... I think you may have timed me just as I was passing a very very slow driver," as I knew he would understand because there are those in this town, who even in a 40 zone, make a point of driving 20. It's not the show of safety they think it is however. It's a show of incapacity that an adult driver isn't even sure enough of their own skill and competence behind the wheel, to bring their vehicle to the fairly rudimentary speed of 40 mph, and still feel in complete control. Such a person is a danger to themselves and others, and should not be permitted on the road. A special motorist rehabilitation class may be needed for such an apprehensive driver.

"But it's a double yellow line, so it wouldn't be legal to pass," he says, still smiling, and with that, putting me at ease in my perturbation.

"Mmm," I say with one eye shut, recognizing there's no path forward to talking my way out of it. He's going to stick me with that ticket, though apparently not charge me for making an admitted illegal pass. He walks to the back of the car to get the license plate number. It's rare that a man in blue gives an unspoken permission to be a little playful when you're pulled over, but sometimes we get a sense of another's sensibilities and mental state enough that customary guidelines of behavior can wiggle a bit.

In this way, police officers and psychologists are trained to be cut from similar cloth, I suppose. Fast instinct to evaluate frames of mind, emotional cadences, and elements of character on a moment's notice.

After checking the license plate, he says, "A 59?" and slowly comes back over to the passenger window. He remains standing upright, which again reveals a remarkably well built 7-foot-tall physique of this particular law enforcement agent. And he ducks back to the window.

"Very beautiful," he says, while making it potentially unclear if he means the car or the girl in it, and tapping on the roof twice with two very large fingers, so much that I notice the amount of noise they produce against the stainless steel. He holds eye contact just a moment longer than necessary to communicate ticketing procedures.

Such acute situational awareness, to use the vernacular of the police, I think, with a playfully raised eyebrow. He's so intent on making his quota, he's stopped the car I passed as well, and is going to nab us both.

I actually spoke to some longtime residents in town who were recounting how the police in the good old days of the city used to be so neighborly in disposition that it sounded like something out of the Andy Griffith show. If you'd had too much to drink, they'd just say "Ok Charlie, let's get you back home" and drive them in the car to safety. Not drive them down to the station to bust them. But of course, everything from education to health care has been equally altered and guided by financial interest, to place business over all else. The only reason naturopathic solutions are so much more expensive than pharmaceuticals is that so-called health care chooses to leverage costs only for industry-based solutions, and not the natural ones that won't addict you or cause prescription interaction complications.

Watching him talk to the driver who was behind me, I smirk. They were slow enough to delay my arrival the first time, I can't believe this is round two of blocking my progress. I hope it's a ticket for obstructing the proper flow of traffic. Mister Police Man has such a very cute butt. Come to think of it, I had a college friend who married the traffic cop who pulled her over. Mmm, I say again.

I will offer this praise for the SFPD, they do take a nonthreatening approach to maintaining the city's police presence in the sense that most patrol cars here actually just say "Public Safety Aide" instead of Police, which is a more accurate title for the job. And we haven't had a law enforcement fatality in the line of duty here since the 1930s, so it's still a little more Andy Griffith than most cities could ever possibly boast.

Officer Jenkins finally hands me my ticket. "Now you be careful out on the road, you hear? Don't want you flying away," he says, looking back over with a wink. I can't help but eye him in the rearview mirror as I start the engine to head back toward town.

  RADIO REPORT: — "Come a Little Bit Closer" by Fleetwood Mac— is on the radio as the engine starts.

If you ever become too deep or serious or mature to have your entire day made, simply by brushing by a breathtaking hottie, whether on the sidewalk, by a coffee counter, or when a seven-foot-tall law enforcement officer pulls you to the side of the road in the middle of nowhere, then you're missing a certain critical feeling for existence. If that's you, allow me to be the one to correctively explode the frustrated neuron-ic signals coursing through your head. Are you too deep to appreciate a sunset? Too mature for the awe of a perfectly arranged plate of victuals? We are made for pleasure, for the licking of frosting from fingers, the wind and sun dancing across our flesh, our feet in motion to the pulsating rhythm of an all-night dance party, the touching of our own earlobes in a quiet reflective moment of repose. Yes, feel yourself flutter from all seven feet of him and be proud that you have a sensuous libido with the blessing of a mammalian desire for touch, and the eyes to lead you to exactly where you can find it.

"My lord," peering back one last time through the mirror, I think, "are these police uniforms intentionally made to produce such a sculpted tailored fit?" I make an incredulous expression as Esmeralda and I speed off with a laugh.

I make up my mind in just that moment of frisson that I will dine alone tonight. If I will be penalized in tickets, then I will also rejoice in lavishness. It will be my maintenance of balance to now dress in queen-like regality with the blouse I've altered to display glamorous puffy green sleeves, while seated in the sunken bar area of The Compound restaurant off Canyon Road. It is in that exact encouched intimacy of conversation with strangers that I will slowly ingest the Butter Capers Chicken, a lunch dish that is secretly available for dinner by special request as a Santa Fe insider option, while quietly pondering in rapt amazement how there are today, people living in our own city, who have never known the joy of having this gastronomic delight enter into their mouths, not even once! I will contemplate the math of that, while smiling and laughing in the pleasure of making new connections, with no particular intention for future renewment, but simply immersed in the joie de vivre of the fleeting and momentary nature of social interplay for its own human sake. But to be clear, at no point losing sight of the present fact that this Butter Capers Chicken, a generously distinguished kiss from culinary witches unknown (to be enjoyed alongside the *Hemingway Daiquiri*, for sure), is so ever present and immediately available, and yet it somehow goes unseen and unknown by so many, night after starry night! It staggers.

And I will be thankful that I am not counted among the unacquainted. For is it unfair, exactly? How this could be overlooked and not experienced by so many... The point here is that it is not. It is the simple benefit and natural reward of paying attention to that which is really all around you.

Just as, after this, I will make my way to Geronimo across the street to indulge in their impeccable desserts and one *Canyon Road Sunset* cocktail with edible flowers, once again ensconced in a hidden bar nook, next to the kiva fireplace filled with little tea candles, which flicker further incantations of bewitchment to the senses.

Santa Fe truly is, at its core, a city of little secrets.

SEQUENCE THIRTEEN

Cybilline's Journal Entry:

Dreamt I was organizing a festival where various firefly tribes were making spectacular formations in the sky. Tracing the emotions I felt about this display, there was a sense of destiny being magnetized together. Separate life journeys and passions, mixing with a divine timing that was connecting all those little but critical dots, like watching active constellations moving into place, taking their positions across the Milky Way, each exerting some subtle influence.

Thinking about the sheer physical beauty of the dream, while I listened to the birds and sat on my little wooden sawhorse bench under the portal, I even talked to the postal carrier about this vision, as he handed me the day's mail. I peered up at the bright sky, thinking about how those same stars we see so clearly at night are all still there the whole day, hidden behind a blinding veil of light.

...Draws mailbox with a fortune cookie sticking out...

He said it was exciting, that maybe I was sensing something big was happening, that a scene would develop that would ripple out, and wouldn't that be what we all needed? I didn't want to get into it, but it's quite the opposite, it's that something little is happening. That it's not about being seen (is that why we call it a 'scene'?) but about seeing better, hearing better, connecting to our information better.

This little point, though, is one of the biggest issues obstructing people's ability to find meaning in their lives and to identify a sense of sustainable purpose. If there's a big scene, it's recognizable; it has form and shape, and people identify it, whereas if it's intimate and personal, it remains amorphous so it's harder to point at and celebrate. But we must! The small conversation in the corner of the room at a party is so often more compelling and eloquent than what most may be paying attention to in the center of the room with all eyes watching. This preoccupation with magnitude is man coping with his cosmic insignificance, the solution to which is in exactly validating that quiet voice, the vast inner world. It is from there that the heart can speak with constellations.

The castle of Kublai Khan in Xanadu, and the entire 16-mile length of the wall that protected the ancient city, built to indulge the Emperor's every fantasy, is now only visible by foot as a small hill covered by grass, and the outline of buildings only visible from the sky. Even the most gilded treasure shall evaporate, the kingdoms, the empires... and yes even constellations themselves, within 100,000 years, gone. Transmuted.

Forever is maybe the silliest word in any language. But we can instead focus on attainable things like having standards, and elevating the moments we do have so that every day is a kind of holiday to celebrate the astounding opportunity we have to simply take action that is our own. To be worthy of cosmic regality.

...Draws a royal crown, with the simple query
'Have You Let Them Convince You That You Are Not A King?'
written in a scroll dangling down the side...

There is a huge percentage of people on this planet for whom success in life simply means finding a mate, securing a job, buying some land, producing offspring, all of which can have validity of course. But at the same time, this quaint view of life's purpose, with visions of 1950s housewives looking longingly out the window for their husband's return from work, is not just a fertile plot for suburban zombie films, but a danger to the species survival.

Since over-population was already a worldwide concern fifty years ago, when the planet's resource-guzzling human habitation was only half of what it's now become, not to mention shocking scenes of starvation and homelessness across American cities everywhere, all while vital planetary reserves are evaporating, the moral imperative of such a reproductive worldview is catastrophic. It is a time where more nuance is asked from humanity, to dig deeper into life's meaning than simply achieving cellular duplication and calling it a purpose.

All the world's inhabitants, whether lichen, oceanic, or those of mammalian origin, are by basic instinct driven to reproduce the cells that ensure the survival of their DNA. But there are higher realms than those dictated to by basic instincts. After all, you can construct novels, make movies, write songs that all carry thought forms that reach millions over the course of many decades and that is another way of transferring your soul mitochondria encoding into the physical species, and which is considerably more powerful and influential than simply breeding a few biological offspring. It can even mean, at an expanded level, co-parenting an entire global generation.

But most animals cannot make art, so they are confined to the providence of mere survivalist toiling. Alternatively, and at the most invisible level, the psychogenetic DNA transfer can be achieved just through the creation of mind waves. By which I not only mean those transfigured by monks in meditation, which they do perform— but the vibrational currents the mind can access, activate, and transmit into the fabric of this very world. Because consciousness is a living thing, and in your interactions with it, you can place seeds of your own beatific resonance across a myriad of dimensions, just by living an interesting life. Without any more achievement than a normal everyday house cat.

...Draws a cat stacked on top of a cat stacked on top of a cat, where each tail becomes a tree with many branches, and apples falling off...

There are so many very, very old ideas, in great need of repair. Part of the woe I see from people is, if they don't have the marriage, the house, the job that does the work of saying your life has meaning, is this ongoing struggle in identifying how the good life is enacted. It has nothing to do with high towers with golden walls, it is instead made up of intangibles. It's something built through your attitude, it's your flair for finding pleasure, it's the care you put into every aspect of how you live. It's your ability to recognize your value; that of your own mind and spirit floating through existence. And to see the god in others. Not necessarily always to see the good in others, as that could be a fairly long wait to find. But it's about your willingness and ability to give yourself permission to reach divine heights, despite whatever anyone else may be reaching for. It's not about heights that other people recognize, ascribe, or assign to you, or praise you for... because ultimately that's THEIR trip. The good life is mostly something you build inside of you.

So I return then, to that other central study of mine: "Does this human culture progress?" Ask Ancient Egypt, which was so sexually permissive that lesbianism was referred to as "the acts of Egypt" and where women were known to have multiple husbands, compared to Egypt today, where belly dancers are sent to prison for undermining family values.

Ask the Roman Empire, after unprecedented prosperity and stability, how it was carved up by warlords and bandits, into 800 years of barbarian grind with illiterate kings, the demise of sophisticated architecture and economic systems, and an absence of the rule of written law. And even at the height of the Roman's dominion, it was a far more depraved period of rule than the Greeks who had preceded them, the inventors of democracy and philosophical ethics.

I think we forget how long we've been at this human game, partly because most of the world still uses the Christian calendar that effectively obscures quite a bit of our post-tribal history, and presents an image to ourselves as being far more virginal than we actually are. There have not just been two centuries of organized civilization bringing us to this point. There were indoor toilets going all the way back to Ancient Egypt, and that is culture enough for me to draw a line in the sand! I mean, around two-thirds of rural Russia today still doesn't have indoor plumbing! Imagine... So that puts the current year at least into the 5100s and yet humanity is still dissected by 200 separately bordered countries, rather than being approximately one freely-accessible world. We are so hopelessly divided.

...Draws a roll of toilet paper that wraps around the Earth...

I drove the other day a mere forty minutes to the Manhattan Project Museum in Los Alamos and saw the letter to the President from Einstein, the scientist's description of the test explosion, and then the pictures of Japan from after the blast... paired with small installations with the jukebox and coffee tables where the secret society of this classified government research lab up in the mountains —then, a hidden town with no zip code— hung out to pass the time. And as I drove out of there back toward Santa Fe, felt the sense of triumph, awe and yet complete horror each person must have felt driving away from that very site after the three year mission was complete.

And thought of the secret projects so many of us work on in our art to further the missions we are called to... for us, of the utmost importance, to direct the world, including our inner world, toward some purposeful future.

Interesting also is how some of those involved thought the explosion might ironically go down in history as a great symbol of peace; that in fighting totalitarianism, ultranationalism, and fascism through this conflict, the horror of the bomb's destruction couldn't paint a clearer, grimmer picture of where violent resolution of conflict leads. But of course, just as the woman I asked on the street about the location of the museum said, "I've been a lifelong resident here and have never been there," we forget... the lesson fades and in that, why recurrence is such a mark of human existence.

Poor memory, for one, but the deeper cause is poor capacity for thinking in the first place. That darn transistor radio and its limited bandwidth of frequencies! Every decade, more followers get together and decide on the new things that are critical to know and learn and absorb for the moment, that represent us figuring it out. Finally! And usually, ten years later shows a good portion of those convictions were obtuse. Yet there is a new moral guard at every turn, which proves as much to be trendy frivolity as the fashions that come and go alongside them.

By which I mean, the 50s, the 60s, the 70s, the 80s, the 90s, all had defining characteristics, that —looking back— cause people to exclaim: "That's what we all thought at that time!" dismissively. And yet fail to ever figure out that our philosophical prejudices of TODAY are just as fraught with fictions that will soon exhaust, as the false ideals that drove every other decade! Not that we shouldn't try. But most of our new social rules are just like those hamsters running on little wheels, going in circles.

I won't say it's a waste of energy to do all that running, because it's all exercise, whether of mind or body! But the fake angst dilemma is simply a rut humanity must find a way out of.

As usual, I deal with the big picture by returning to the individual. Because humanity can't break a rut, but you can. And it's probably something I end up going over with all my clients at some point: that we can break ruts in so many ways. When you feel stuck in the same old routines and can't seem to access a fix, try a more metaphysical approach. Just loosening the grip of your existing patterns, as a way of wiggling the invisible threads that our habits attach to and hang upon. You can drive to work taking a different route, change the order of something you commonly do like how you put on your makeup, or intentionally shop at the grocery beginning from the opposite aisle you normally start in. In other words, whatever habit you've gotten into, start with the ripple in the pond effect and open the door to energetically inviting change. Maybe you can get unstuck indirectly, by breaking a rut from unrelated areas of your life, unrelated areas of consciousness. If we can get our brain into the 'let's try something new' frame of mind, all of those neuro-receptors are connected.

...Draws an empty train track with a cloud above it,
and a flying saucer hiding above that...

In the end, we are all secretly conductors of energy, and must learn how to turn our own lights on.

SEQUENCE FOURTEEN

Cybilline lay her silky soft blonde hair on the satin sheet pillows and looks up at the late afternoon sun streaming in through the skylight in her bedroom. One of the delights in living in an adobe home is the common placement of these windows that lets the light in from above, and not just along the middle of the wall, that makes you feel a little less separated from the outside environment.

Her fingers caress her soft hands, feeling the miraculous textures of the skin that envelopes the sweet corporeal vessel. Delighting in the curves of the body, down the neck and around the chest, fingertips glide on these warm supple surfaces, that seem to speak back in response, and elevate all the senses to something approaching an orchestral rush.

The experience of blouse buttons opening is the birth of emotion, releasing up and around the figure on the bed. The facades of our daily negotiations with the outside world, peel away as the body is set free from confinements. Reaching down to caress the kneecap and slowly up the thigh, a fingernail digs into flesh, and the skin returns a thankful glow. As garments let go from a tug at the waist, pure sensation co-mingles with the radiator visions of thought, and rises steam-like to primacy.

The electric wires and strings that maintain physical space palpate with momentary experience, and reality becomes an animated feature, with marks drawn by hand, then splattered in powders, jetting out of the lines. Breathing becomes heavier, rhythmic, the pores open like a thousand mouths. Cartoon fireflies, rushed with energy from the aroma of a pheromone release, blink and emanate soft hues, receiving signals and sending them out into the air, circling the head like a tall occult crown, as her fingers move in spiral rotations.

The lights settle into the glow of a pinball machine, as the female form in the encased cabinet has legs that spread, and the ball hits the sensors as the ringer goes ping ping ping.

  RADIO REPORT: WHILE A STRING OF RADIO ADS HAVE PLAYED QUIETLY FOR LOCAL CAR SALES, THE STATIC CLEARS ON THE TRANSISTOR RADIO IN THE KITCHEN, SEEMINGLY RECEIVING A STRONGER SIGNAL FROM ANOTHER STATION AS THE BASS LINE OF — "SHE BOP" BY CYNDI LAUPER— PLAYS WITH CLARITY PAST THE RADIO FOG.

The ball is slapped back into play, rolling across the stretchy rubber slingshots, connecting the pathways while the roving circular dome travels as it WOOOWWWWWS around a hole and bounces up and down into that spot, as the score goes higher 100 points, 200, 300. The ball pops up and out and rolls across the humming arenas of the mounted board, the sound of its movement almost anticipatory, UUHHHHH it hits the side wall and PING PING PING the sound shrieks as lights flash and score reels go up and up, while the ball hits a bumper and zips away toward more open territory. The legs close and spread again.

The flippers slap and pound, redirecting the ball across the field of play, popping at the scoring target of a girl's anatomy, with velocity and spin. The animated mouth opens in a full circle, eye plates behind eye lashes roll upward and white lights flash around the pupils, as PING PING PING the ball circles the hole again, dips in, and sinks with full weight, amply filling the ignited orifice. Center bull's eye target strike. Score. 500 points.

Then the silver orb is grabbed as if by storm from a whirlwind vortex, and tossed in an unexpected crosscurrent direction, leaning into a crevice which causes the ball to spin, each rotation adding more points. Then traveling through an inclined plane down the ramp, and SLAP! back against the flipper that swats and spanks. The cheeks become rosy.

She grabs a toy from the dresser because tools aren't just for gardening anymore. The toes curl, as electromagnets play havoc with the speed of the roving ball. The eye winks. The electric circuits cause the flesh to quiver.

There's a knock at the door. Everything suddenly stops. She cranes her neck and listens to be sure. Knock knock again. Her eyes squint. "Isn't this why I live alone?" she says to herself, almost a query to the spirits, annoyed. "OK! COMING!" she yells.

Cybilline quickly pulls her clothes back on, hopping up on the bed, to help her thrust upward to her feet, leaving behind a technicolor world of anime distortions in favor of the literal handle she twists to open the door.

"Special delivery," the mailman says. "I hope it's worth interrupting my book," Cybilline huffs, grabbing the pen. Realizing it's not his fault that her energy is like a buzzing hive, she exhales and smiles, "Just kidding."

"Had any more dreams?" he asks. "*OOO!* Not a *one!*" she squeals, quickly rerouting the energy of conversation to the bottle in her hand as she pulls it from the container. "This is the olive oil I ordered! Mmm!" She holds the box up and exaggerates her smile as she closes the door. She eyeballs the contents of the Mythology Extra Virgin Olive Oil from Greece that she had found out was served at La Boca, after being given incorrect information three times.

Tsk, tsk, she thinks of any attempt to keep her from her gravy. She gets what she's after, even if the achievement is simply a more divine bite of crumbs.

SEQUENCE FIFTEEN

I woke up to the sound of clanking in the kitchen and the water running. I press my fingers to my temples and slowly breath out. In no alarm at this intrusion at all, I push the sheets away and stumble over to the sink.

"Cybilline, what a pleasure to wake up to," I say to the golden-haired woman doing the dishes. "Angus you have to stop living like this..." she says, "there's only so much ignoring a set of coffee cups can handle before they simply disintegrate."

"How'd you get in here anyway?" and she looks back over at me, and though the recognizable blonde hair is as perky as ever, her face is bright turquoise colored.

"You let me in," she says. Squints her eyes as if peeking into a mystery and shakes her head. "How much did you drink last night exactly?" I squint back. Her skin IS blue. For some reason I still haven't commented on this.

"I could never not let you in," I tell her with some possible subtle slyness on my part, "but..."

"But?" she replies... then matter of factly blurts, "Isn't everything glorious?" Her blue eyes and blue skin are in amazing proximity of shade, with her eyes slightly winning out in depth of color. I still say nothing of this.

"It is, it is," I reply, "but you know, I want to talk about something I'm wondering about." She puts her hand under her chin like Rodin's The Thinker, but much hotter, and blue. She just looks so tranquil and gorgeous; I almost don't want to disturb her. "Do you ever feel... not of this world?" I semi-whisper to begin my inquiry, and then sit cross-legged on the couch, looking up at her.

"Well," she says, and sits on the edge of the sofa arm, putting her hands in my hair and stroking my head in a calming way. Her fingers have such good energy in them and I like to be pet like a dog. All guys do. "That's complicated. Who we are shifts, so whether you belong to a world or not, may shift too. But I wouldn't say it's a bad thing to feel alien to anything, really, for a time..."

"Yeah, embracing the weird is along the lines of what I'm thinking," I tell her. "It's like, underneath all our hidden layers, no one is ordinary. That's always just a cover. Because the universe is strange and magnificent, and that means we are too."

"Hidden layers, indeed," she chirps. "Humanity has been around long enough now to be displayed in fossilized form!"

At that moment, I literally see all of human history in my mind as an encased fossil, including trees we've been housed under, spells we've fallen under, and even all the wars for territory we've fought, that have determined the entire geography of the planet's nations. Bloodshed communicated by adhesive vinyl Colorforms. "But part of that hiding," she suggests, "under the trappings of ordinariness, and fitting-in-ness, is something shocking: a suffocating of the real self, an avoidance of hearing our own voice! Because if you hear it, you may have to listen to it. And that's work."

"That IS work," I say in agreement, moving closer to her, both for a sense of comradery and to sniff the air around her. "But such a price to pay to avoid it!" She nods at my assertion, and offers back without delay, "It's the norm. But there's a simple trick to cut through all those layers." I raise my eyebrows and watch her blue lips say, "Simply making a decision to not live in fear. It's not so much an issue of people not knowing themselves as it is a lack of bravery. To act on it. People *dream* of what they want to do all the time."

"That's why we're artists. That's what it's for," I say, lifting my hands toward the heavens. "The art builds you as you build the art. And we refine our self-knowing by making it," I continue in my favorite topic of oration. "Your art isn't a picture, it's your voice asserting itself."

"But how to get people to recognize there's that value in it?" Cybilline says with a sigh. "It's easy to see the value in eating. Even exercising is more easily valued, which is far less important than art for quality of life and developing the richness of your psyche," she says, with a hint of amazement that this subtle distinction of value goes so unrecognized by so many. "There are seven million species of animal currently living on this planet, and they're an expression of the creative force of this cosmos, a force that we have the power to connect to." Her voice rises. She would be a great actress.

"And utilize," I add, as if we are fomenting a revolution. "Whenever someone says they don't believe in alien life, I ask if they've ever looked at what lives in our oceans. Those aquatic lifeforms are just a small hint at the diversity of manifestation that is out there." I look at the black nail polish on my living room table, and think about applying it as the base for what could become a finger-based canvas of faraway stars.

"Ha! Yes," Cybilline says with a relaxed smiling mouth, which I watch with intent. "That's really the pool to jump into!" Her eyes smolder like they're contemplating something delicious. "If you can link creative energy to space, it goes back to your original idea about not being from this world. Or needing to be! It's a gateway to release the basic assumption that Earth, this world, is your central source— when you can connect to the Cosmos as being your home, rooting yourself into an entirely larger sense of place, or belonging. That anywhere in the galaxy, you are home. Earthlings are so hopelessly Earthbound!"

"That's it!" I cry. "It doesn't even matter whether you're from another world or this one, you just exist in space and time." She's nodding a dreamy yes. She looks at me like a piece of meat. Or she might say, with intrigue. But this is my chapter.

"And unlike any other that came before," I add. Meaning, especially her.

"Well... of course there's some natural fear of uniqueness," she concedes, "because it separates us from the herd, and as an animal, that is dangerous. But how," she wonders, "can people doubt their originality and think they're just like everybody else, when you can look through volume after volume of photography monographs, newspaper clippings, historical records— scan the crowds! And you'll never see anyone, other than identical twins, who come from the same fertilized egg, that have the same face as anyone you've ever known. Consider how miraculous that is. Like music, which has only seven chords and yet out of that basic configuration, springs endless combinations. No song ever being the same, never duplicating. While a human face also has seven variables; two eyes, two ears, a nose, a mouth, and some hair... and yet," she says mystified, "endless combinations across those fairly limited square inches of face, producing 100 billion unique looks. How can it be."

I love to listen to her lecture. She processes so many odd statistical facts and scribbles those and other weird notations in her journal. I've seen it. Like she's a social scientist collecting information, on... us. This world. Other worlds too, I suppose. But I know what at first seems like a tangent with her is just a very long sentence with lots of details that express a fuller picture. She likes short answers but only if they're good enough.

"Part of why I'm asking about this world and other worlds, is that I've been obsessing lately about the Sixth Extinction," I tell her. "When you said the thing about viewing us in fossilized form..." and I laugh. "Well, there have been five already, and we're apparently entering the sixth."

Cybilline has moved back to the sink and starts placing the washed mugs back into the cupboard. I turn on the Bluetooth sound system in my kitchen from my phone and click Spotify's Weekly Discoveries playlist, as she continues to consider the cosmos and our place in it.

RADIO REPORT: —UNKNOWN EXPERIMENTAL JAZZ WITH AFRO-CUBAN RHYTHMS— PLAYS.

"I mean... there ARE other worlds," she calls, raising her voice over the music, "and civilizations regularly perish. Did you know, a star explodes every second somewhere in the universe. And even in death, stars are reborn, sowing new worlds just as plants spread their lifeline through a proliferation of seeds."

She has what appears to me to be little sparks of light gathered around her turquoise complexion, and her eyes have almost a swimming quality in their blue spiral pools, looking out at me. She puts her hands on my shoulder. "...But if you're really nervous about it, you just have to remember that you don't have to survive in this form in order to exist."

"I don't?" I say back and she is nodding no, like I'm a silly silly boy. "You don't," she assures. Then she seems to spread her arms like wings, and dances to an internal music, which I can totally relate to. I'm going to dance with her. She playfully taps my nose with her finger like a modern-day Tinker Bell, and I feel the electric current of one form intersecting with another.

We are flowing and floating in space together. I am giving myself over to that wavelength, and feel as if we are touching each other in non-physical habitats as we move, and yet I keep wanting to not forget to finish the conversation. "Like, what form... would I take?" I say. She looks over like she has no idea that we have been on any topic. Then she shakes her head, like I've made the goddess come down to Earth from giving cosmic lectures in Zeus's heavenly hallways. "You have a whole soul network..." she shrugs. "You can transcend the parameters of this life and draw in experiences, particles of knowledge, and even applicable skills and sensibilities, from your many incarnations hidden in the universe's energetic records, just like your own subconscious," she says. "You could be somewhere else just as much as you can be here." She returns to dance. I think Shiva would be jealous of her dexterity.

As I watch her move, I think the whole conversation is about freedom. How we can tap into our DNA like a branch, to release more of the hidden flora dormant in our cells, and activate anthesis, the sprouting of the flower bud. And few ever register this, but flowers are the genitals of plants. And most flowers contain both male and female parts, which just makes existence that extra bit kinkier. It gives me such an idea for a new tattoo.

I'm recalling Cybilline as she was driving us out to Ojo, with her back arched, leaning forward against the steering wheel, unconstrained and singing in the car, with the wind in her hair and the sun coming through the windshield and onto her mouth, as she let those notes loose from her lips. Yes, an open flower bud, and free. Her spirit was inside and outside her body, all at once.

"You know people astral project, right?" she says, making the softest flowing motions with her hands, because the music just feels really good this morning. "They leave their bodies." She comes back over and adds, "We could leave our bodies" in the same tone you might say we could go to dinner.

"I have read about that," I tell her, "I mean, it's not something I've successfully done." I instinctually place my hand on my throat, not sure how much to say, to reveal. My hand on the larynx comforts. In truth, I find most touch comforts.

"I believe in cosmic consciousness, but I want to admit there's always a nagging question in my mind about it, to see evolution as a social force, when we're surrounded by so much lack of it, all the time!

People get wrapped up in ideologies, from the culture or the religion or whatever system has told them what's worth getting riled up over, from the moment they wake up to putting on their pajamas at night; just an infomercial of misinformation," I say, to vent some of my frustration with society, that I never know quite what to do with. It's like some static in between stations on the radio. "I wonder if a whole life could just all be wasted existence."

"You can just say 'bless you' to the bullshit and raise the vibration all the way around, so that's one strategy. But yes, ideologies can be so tragic," she speaks without the light-heartedness of before, "like Gerhard Richter's photorealism series, *October 18, 1977*, where he painted those photos of young terrorist's dead bodies that appeared in the newspaper after they'd been shot. Such haunting paintings..."

"That sounds unbelievably morose," I say, feeling strangely unprotective of my space, watching her search my things, having no idea what she's hunting for. She's touching corners of things, slightly lifting them, peeking into spaces.

"No, he didn't paint them for any exploitative reason, but out of sadness, that they died so senselessly, just due to an ideology they got wrapped up in... That they died so young," she repeats, with a pause "...they died for nothing."

I look the series up on my phone, and as I scroll, mention, "He's German." She nods yes without looking at me as she pulls a sleeve on one of my shirts. "I have a book of an amazing German photographer Karlheinz Weinberger, you know of it?" She shakes her head in the negative, and I say with sudden excitement to share this, "He took photos of these gangs," and I stand up, darting over to the bookshelf. "But they were almost like fashion gangs! They were kind of ruffians but very into Elvis Presley, and would write his name down their pants and..." "Whaat?!" she interrupts, "Where are these photographs?" Yes, I think with satisfaction, a new connective fascination has been triggered. I hand over the goods to her.

Her blue fingers against the black and white photos is thrilling to me. I might just have to ask her about the skin thing now, but I keep hesitating. Truth is, I'd rather be mystified than have answers.

She has so many subtle fragrances that hit you at different moments, she is like a pheromone activation center. I lean in as she scans the pages.

RADIO REPORT: — "OUTER SPACE" BY JOHN GRANT—RADIATES OUT OF THE KITCHEN SPEAKERS.

"This," she says pointing at a boy with an almost life size Elvis-head belt buckle and string tying the crotch up, "is what so many miss out on."

"Miss by choice!" I specify.

"I *meannn*," she lilts, "a lot of youth should just be spent discovering your beauty as a soul and exploring that, and nurturing that. Investigating life's subtle poetic articulations. To be young and just join the workforce, and have your primary focus be the demands of some job, entirely in service of another's interests... and not spend time being this beautiful... is ridiculous." She shakes her head. "This is the greatest gang in the world."

"It's definitely the only gang I could have ever joined," I say laughing. "A gang of oddball outsider punk fashion extremists." Then feel the need to clarify, "You understand when I say they miss being that by choice, I mean it's a shame people aren't cool enough to generally do that stuff."

"Yeah," she assures, "I think I get you, Angus," with her patented sudden eye contact, followed by the slightly upcurved smile that's impossible to decipher. Then she looks back at the art. There is an aura of peace surrounding us.

And I so appreciate her enthusiasm about these photos. But I am also determined to return to the issue of meaninglessness that has been dogging me, even though I have fun despite it. And yes, sometimes because of it. "So if someone lives with purely borrowed thoughts, believing in them fully, how is their lifetime even useful to their evolution? How is there meaning from that?"

"It does have meaning," she says, "even if it seems like all their thoughts are fantasies."

"It's NOT a fantasy??!!" "No it IS. But it's a fantasy with a function."

Cybilline has somehow found my stash of little drums, and I'm amazed at how much ground she's covered in my small casita. She now starts tapping on them with her Shiva-reflective fingers. I wonder, when has she ever been so distractible yet so focused, at the same time. She resumes her articulation.

"The energetics of your desire to be true, the discipline required of you to do without something —due to a belief you uphold— and the fortitude to fight your way through... those are all real. Finding forgiveness. Sacrifice. You may one day see past the things you once made sacrifices for and change direction entirely, but if those times of self-discipline help show you what you're capable of, shows you your capacity, then that becomes an important part of who you are. So the particulars can be an illusion, but the internal subjective reality has objective value."

"The subjective has... objective value," I replay the words aloud.

"It's why the unicorns didn't get on Noah's Ark," she says like an extremely innocent girl. "That would've meant they mistook physical reality as being real, instead of knowing it was maya."

I get up from the couch and go to the mirror to straighten my hair and lift my jaw a bit to look at the angle on my aging face. A few years yet till 40 but maybe I look better now than ten years ago, I think. I'm convinced of it. The way I live has imprinted itself in my facial morphology. It's as if my younger looks were missing a component, incomplete. I peek over at Cyb real quick. It's fun to look at each other and see from her pupils, how she likes what she sees and can see me looking back, liking what I see. There's such a rush in that.

I look back over at her, this time peering behind me, from through the mirror, and Cybilline has a huge white horn jetting upward from between her temples. Elegant and bestial at the same time. I slowly turn around, and she catches my eye. No horn. I smile. She smiles. I turn back to the mirror. In the reflection she also has a whole garland of blue flowers around her empyrean neck, and her beauty is magnified from a perfect 10 to a 15 Squared. Her eyes, full of such a serenity, that nothing could possibly disturb or ruffle her. Because it is all so trivial in comparison to the light.

So many women seem to need assurances when I get involved with them, which tends to increase with time. And her not needing them from me seems to make me want assurances myself. Yet I especially like that she needs her space and freedom, while still embracing our attachment. "Attachment... and freedom ...can go hand in hand, can't they?" she has said to me more than once. "Oh absoluuutely," I tend to reply with enthusiasm. But I still wonder, and I call over to her, "Hey doll, ya ready to go steady?" I grab my cowboy hat from the coat rack and putting it on, give her a dashing stare.

She smiles like I've said something flattering. I think I almost caught a blush. But of course her cheeks can't transition to another primary color with blue as its base, so it's hard to tell.

"Steady?" she says like I've suggested playing a new game that she's unfamiliar with. "We've been plenty steady. If you mean your one and only, let's just say, how I might approach finances, squirreling away resources, is not how I would approach romance." "What does that mean exactly?" I say with a half squint of the eye, not entirely ready for her response but ready enough. She then goes to the window where the light leans into the room beaming across her fantastically oval bosoms. She seems to do it all perfectly without ever trying, everything just lands right. "When it comes to my car, I believe in ownership," she continues to try to illustrate.

"Ahh," I say, "but not when it comes to people." "No... I don't like my freedom of movement curtailed, nor do I believe that represents security," she says, with a pause and an exhale. "I just don't think it's necessary... Do you?"

I pause in my reply because I'm game for how she wants to play it. She's not the type of woman who needs a man to make her heart run wild. She's got her own thing. And for myself, I suspect I haven't entirely examined all the writing in the smaller print of my encoding, and the connection I find with her may be something that requires some bravery, and injecting that confidence into my hidden emotional fear, right there in the sticky part we all avoid.

"I mean, sure it's a commodity world, you want and so you own," she declares, placing her fingers warmly across her shoulder. "But does loving something mean owning it?" She pauses thoughtfully and exhales again, then looking me squarely in the eye, says "I like you free... a lot," stepping forward toward me slowly. "Do you like me free?"

It just becomes so clear. Who would want to try to capture and control that, when her autonomy is so central to what makes her so alluring. It'd be like putting a firefly in a jar.

Most of us feel all alone in the universe and want someone there to end the loneliness. But Cybilline is not alone... She feels connected to everything. And if it's not loneliness people fear, then it's freedom. But in a way, what's more glamorous than the honesty of being alone in the universe? That's where you meet the Creative Force of Everything, flesh to flesh, finger touching finger. And where we stand apart from all other creation is also where our uniqueness truly announces itself. We all have a little something that no one else has, starting with our fingerprints.

When Cybilline demands some solitary agency, it's part of her otherness, her outsider presence no matter the environment. She could never entirely fit into any group, always slightly in between this category or that one. Maybe if she were on a different planet, among a different species...

I look up and her ocean eyes are just inches from me, as if she had read my thoughts. She kisses my cheek, and I wake up, startled. I could hear the garbage truck outside, with its hydraulic powered arm pouring the large blue pale's contents into the hopper, and crashing them back to the ground, emptied.

I touch my face. Like being awakened from a dance with an apparition and having nothing but the warm dew, fresh upon your cheek, as evidence that anything may have occurred at all.

Back in her casita, Cybilline Farroh's soft blue eyes blink open.

SEQUENCE SIXTEEN

So many mornings, those fireflies have been released by that hand. It's remained a mysterious curiosity for me so many times. But this morning I saw something startling; that they are my own fingers opening the jar, setting those little twinkling bodies free into the day. Like lightning, short and long flashes in the air, without any sound, speaking a language of illumination.

And then I picked up the hand mirror from off the bedside table and noted the bioluminescence of a very bright scattering of fluttery wings, which was no trick of the light. I really did catch a glimpse!

I also couldn't help but notice though, there had to be nearly 160 fireflies now— Almost too many to be contained by that jar...

SEQUENCE SEVENTEEN

Slowly taking my first sips of Black Lightning, I am inspired by the idea that despite so many differences in belief, tolerance, and lifestyles, that the people of the world are united by that ritual of drinking morning coffee together, all across the globe. Of course I fully realize that morning is happening at all hours of the day, and that in reality, more people on this planet drink tea and eat bugs than drink coffee. But I'll stand by my original intent on this one.

And as I indulge, in continued agreement with these sentiments, I flip through art books and allow that flow of images to serve as a form of meditation. I look not just at the paintings, but try to peer behind the scenes, imagining the steps involved in how it was constructed and search for the artist's hand behind the brushstroke. This puts me in a state of mind that, when I process the experiences of my clients over the afternoon, already has me somewhat occupying their mindset; that of an inventor's world.

Today, I've planned a quick pit stop at Kakawa Chocolate House for one of their warm sipping chocolate elixirs. These historic concoctions are a Santa Fe tradition, using herbs, flowers and spices mixed in warmed drinking dark chocolates, to recreate unique sippables based on recipes dating back from pre-Columbian and Mesopotamian times, up to the sixteenth century. I always pick the ones that feature aphrodisiacs because if given a choice, why would you not? But I don't think that's just a modern sensibility, since so many thousands of years ago, mortals often had sensuous relationships with the gods, in a mutual quest for sexual satiety. Another good reason to create your own deities.

To heighten the mood that those elegant libations will set, I go slightly out of my way for an aesthetic lift, as I often do, by driving into town by way of Camino del Monte Sol, providing a view of the most charming stretch of classic adobe homes between Camino del Poniente and Camino Santander. There are so many jaw-dropping stretches of properties in the area, but this one has really caught my fancy. To think there are people out there in the world struggling with finding some meaning in life, and meanwhile there are people living in these wonderful structures that exemplify the Santa Fe dream of adobe bliss, which may in fact BE the meaning of life. I cut across Acequia Madre toward Paseo de Peralta, to get over to Kakawa, hoping especially for something infused with rose and damiana.

  RADIO REPORT: — "Mirrors" by Galactic Witchcraft—plays as I make the drive over.

When I turn into the parking lot, delectability is the first lifestyle choice on my agenda, but relaxation commingled with stimulation is not far behind. This is preparatory mood work in advance of an appointment at the Santa Fe Salt Cave. A town never averse to invention through artful fabrications, this salt cave certainly treads the line between authentic natural healing destination and art project. Since I see art project as another form of natural healing anyway, I am only doubly excited by this. Halotherapy, or salt therapy known by a broader terminology, involves releasing thousands of tiny particles of salt into the room, which clears your skin, sinuses, inflammation in the lungs, and most importantly, quiets your mind and creates a feeling of well-being. This man-made cave was created from nine tons of pink salt crystals repurposed from the Himalayan mountains, which entirely cover the walls and floor, with subtle lights highlighting the crystalline qualities of the hard cave surfaces, and a hint of space music in the background that sometimes takes on the subtle sonic ambience of being electrical transmissions. As an explorer of sounds, I can't help but support this affectation disguised as cosmological phenomenon.

The fact that this gem of relaxation exists in a remarkably nondescript strip mall of pedestrian stores made of cheap metal siding, is part of its charm, but the kind of transparent construct that throws those confined by the buzzwords of authenticity into a tizzy. Yes, it's a portal in a shopping mall. Hard to believe for some that it's in these places with an appearance of the lowbrow and 'everyday' that the spectacular often gathers between the walls. That you don't need to travel to a pristine destination in the mountains of Sedona to find energy vortexes, and that these pockets of magic can be constructed by actual human intent and ingenuity. That a rundown and discarded location can be a secret playground for pixies.

My client Cecilia was in a session just last week telling me about her distrust of cheaply made wonders, which speaks to this.

FLASHBACK TO THERAPY SESSION: "I was out looking at jewelry at one of the fairs over the weekend, and I had it in my mind that I'd get some kind of rosary bead necklace, which I just mean for aesthetics," she says, motioning with her arms to indicate lack of belief in any non-aesthetic uses. "I had seen them in a window at the Loretto and have to admit they felt kind of sexy," she giggled, "like I wanted them for some blasphemic purpose. Something attractive in them, despite what they are intended for, you know? They're sexy." She looked over at me very quickly to be sure I believed her, which I did, and looked back out the window. After all, Madonna used them similarly 40 years ago, so it's not exactly shocking. "So I was looking for a less pricey version, but these were really just cheaply made," she said, "I could see the string through the beads, even though they were still admittedly charming," she continued. "So even though I was looking for something inexpensive, that doesn't mean cheap. I couldn't trust that it had value or any real power to it, because I knew it wasn't quality."

"But I don't agree with that," I told her. "It depends on who is making it, and what qualities they infuse in it. And why does the ingenuity required to make something from modest resources not have a high value, or even a certain special power?"

In fact, when inventiveness rather than finance is used to construct something, perhaps it should hold a greater place of honor in the heart. When it comes to ritual, the personal touch unquestionably provides a stronger signal. That's why music made inexpensively by the right artist, with the right presence and intention, can move millions of people, while music made with millions of dollars behind it, can hold no soul or power in it at all. Magic after all works by mysterious pathways, by its very nature.

Still some will proclaim "How can it be authentic... HERE?" in a brutal failure of imagination, looking at this mall of such barren appearance.

First, I think it's important to recognize that where the term authentic is concerned in this town, it is often a word reserved for grandma's age-old recipes, making something exactly the way it's been prepared for generations. It's certainly a point of contention, as that "authentic cooking" implies that anyone who may have traveled the world and brought their culinary experiences here to share, do NOT fit in an exalted category by these standards. As though the skill set of these well-traveled gourmands, who have learned secrets from experts around the globe who have dedicated their lives to the finer intricacies of cuisine, and who have come to live in Santa Fe, are less a culinary treasure than your grandmother and the limited resources she created meals with, from nearly before the advent of the freight train.

We all have a grandmother who has recipes. Yours is not special.

But don't get me wrong. I love that people honor their ancestors to such a brazen extent, and history buffs would be thrilled, but it's not hard to pick up on the patterns that speak to romanticization more than anything resembling accuracy. It's part of an intriguing tendency of an almost worshipful reverence for the past that you tend to hear people recount. Perhaps the past charms because it's already happened and therefore has no new challenge to live up to associated with it, and so contains a certain serene peace. But what's striking for me is that it's the remarkable ordinariness that seems to captivate. For instance, you will hear people say in an almost starry-eyed state of adoration how they loved the olden days when they would get sopapillas and sit on the steps of the railyard, dipping them in honey and eating them with their friends, enjoying the sun and light breezes. It's not exactly a memory of being on a cruise ship in the 80s off the coast of Hawaii doing cocaine with Stevie Nicks, the white witch of rock 'n' roll and one of the patron saints of neo-modern Santa Fe sensibilities. By setting such a proportionally simple bar for halcyon days, I'm tempted to wonder "Why don't you buy a batch of sopapillas right now, and sit in the sun with a few friends on the steps of the railyard, dipping them in honey?" After all, any day is a fine day for creating such happy memories.

At the same time, the astounding distinctness of Santa Fe can't help but permeate like molasses and cinnamon even these moments of relative ordinaire. Because sopapillas are an invention that results specifically from the unique cross-pollination of Spanish and Native American Indian influences upon the culture of New Mexico. It's a deep-fried gastronomic warm pocket of a treat that combines elements of the Spanish churro and buñuelo with the quite satisfying Indian puffed fry bread. And it's true, dip it in honey and you're home free to a childlike place of innocent comforts.

Now, not all things from the past are cherished: some do critique the older retirees for aging the demographics of this city. But it is not the play of youth but the charm of long contemplation and ultimate acceptance that lines these streets, and the city sells and markets itself on its historic quality. If we could all just gracefully fall into disrepair the way so many structures here do, then we're assured a senescence we can be proud of. Yet in a way, the "oldest" thing to me about Santa Fe, and it being stuck in some curious irrelevance of concern, is that glorification by locals about your neighbors being the same people as they've been through generations past. When by comparison, a New Yorker would know, they are all just people... and there's nothing special —or even authentic— about the fact of coming from only one type of background. People with traveling roots would in fact tend to be more authentic to the true human character, because those are folks that have been guided by the diversification of experience and the challenges to taste and identity that those engagements bring. They aren't less real, but more real. New Yorkers look forward to people coming in to amplify the possibilities presented by the widest cross-section of humankind possible, and making that very infusion part of the "local culture."

To be fair, Santa Fe does 'permit otherness' admirably in a sense, because here, the more playfully outlandish and eccentric you are, the more people dig it. That's not the norm for a relatively small-town population, where 'different' would usually be perceived as, and treated as, threatening. But the day-to-day culture here, and not that of the short-term stay tourist, is still unquestionably in a state of balancing a trust between old influences and new ideas.

This is all to say, I am a believer in the Santa Fe Salt Cave, which may be blasphemic to nature lovers everywhere! But if you're insulted by that, I'll take it even a step further: I'm a believer as much as I believe in van Gogh's The Starry Night or Monet's Water Lilies. The day I see water lilies anywhere in the natural world that can match Monet's representative construction of them, through oil paint on canvas, in their dreamlike grandiose beauty, we can talk about whether earthlings have the power of magic within us to place true windows to the galaxy in a strip mall. But it will only cost you a third of the price of a traditional massage to find out for yourself about the wondrous relaxation it provides.

After removing my shoes in the reception area, and taking a seat in the zero gravity chairs on the sandy floor, there is already a sense of serenity kicking in. That very faint electronic space music and the blinking of stars in the fabricated ceiling sky, are effective in blanketing the mind to quietude. Being placed in a state of consciousness that simply allows you to listen, to become receptive to the wavelengths of thought that usually only your unconscious mind is receiving.

It's why someone should never be shamed for occasionally sitting around doing nothing. Tuning into the cosmos requires just that and is very much doing something.

Today is especially fortunate, because none of the other eight chairs are occupied for the hourly appointment, and so not even the minor distraction of someone shuffling in their seat will be present. Ahh, to be alone in paradise! The attendant closes the door for the salt therapy to commence.

As I lean back, I experience a near immediate shift in beta waves. In my mind's eye, I am wearing a white leather aviation helmet and long knee-high red boots, the captain of a single-passenger DNA Psyche Converter machine.

"Cybilline, are your monitors registering fully?" the transistor voice says over the intercom of astral imagining. I click on some switches, the red, the green, the purple, the blue. Click! Click! The windshield of the craft is actually a beauty mirror, emitting just the right lighting to observe my features for proper maintenance. This meditative trance is a looking glass for the application of our very own cellular makeup, an internal alchemical facial.

You might be led by my general appearance to believe I'm a real fashionista, but I'm not. I'm a real funista, in part due to learning that what many take seriously shouldn't be, and what many don't take seriously, often should. Some think that fun is frivolous, but it is very very serious. Look at the almost religious fervor that people experience around their favorite bands (we call the performance of music "playing") and sporting events. It's about the celebration of being. That's not found in formalwear; in fact that stuffy pomp is often enacted in reverence to the trivial and discardable. Writing a song is serious.

Who knows what glory will be unleashed when ivory keys are tickled across a piano! Sometimes just listening to logic is too earnest an approach, because logic even at its best, only knows so much. Room must be made for the ruleless. So there were never any special workouts or eating of leafy greens in my beauty maintenance for a youthful appearance, but my anti-aging workouts have been geared toward clearing mental processes, and actively blocking the weight of false pressures that encumber, a mind over matter approach that has kept me uncommonly preserved.

And that is what I am here for today, as the DNA Psyche Converter goes into full activation. The stars of the ceiling blink, the call of lifetimes lived in many galaxies, and not just the sounds of this planet, of this day's newspaper, are permitted to come into focus. I smile. The clearing away of stresses all starts with the maintenance of your own frame of mind, in recognizing that no one is more subjected to the mood you're in than you are. We often think we're punishing someone with our bad mood but really, it's just us carrying it. Holding the anger, internalizing the tension. But you CAN control the weather of your inner world, and you owe it to yourself to let the sunlight in and the storm clouds fade into the background.

Ask your five-year-old self about this, she who just wants to play, and is not deterred by all the contentious news of the world, most of which is crap anyway. Grab her hand as your protector, for she is a warrior to your Ever-Renewal. It is she who exists prior to the forgetting that accompanies worldly immersion— the part of you that starts to believe you are your name, your birthday, your social security number, and not some multidimensional mythological creature.

It could be theorized that even mythological creatures connect to the magic of their early existence, even when they are millions of years old. There must be a place of innocence, somewhere, in their developmental curve, where an unhampered purity pours forth. And they manage to hold onto that point of activation, always.

Once you experience your first pain is when you erect your first wall to protect yourself; the beginning of shutting something down that must always remain open. Whatever struggles we have, after all, are just tools that our spirits use to map out our liberation.

I lean back in the chair and meditate on an experience when I felt unencumbered by any expectation, any criticism, any awareness that something I might do could be perceived as not good enough. That if I sat and made a drawing, that it could be beautiful simply because those colors were how I felt, and whatever I felt was holy. I think of how that receptivity feels and close my eyes, sending the energy of that feeling of openness into all the cells in my body, from my toenails to my knees to my lungs to my follicles to my throat to my ears. I illuminate all my energy centers with this feeling of being unguarded with pure impulse and lightness. I smile, imprinting the trust of that experience and I teach all of my cells to remember this feeling, in their encoding.

It is important to recognize the invaluable role of fantasy in healing. Many a rock star's fuel to ascension has been magnified by this resource. A key factor in utilizing these life invention skills effectively is simply to identify which events and conversations are pertinent for review, knowing which to take ownership of and which to release. As I think this, a pair of golden goggles materialize under my helmet and I go deeper into self-hypnosis.

I think of a time when someone disappointed me, something that closed my heart to some degree. And I apply this technology of consciousness to that troubling experience. I see an alternate reality of possibility where I was not disappointed, instead. Where I was rewarded. How many of our experiences could have randomly gone another direction, and had a different result. Yet we take it for reality when in fact it "just happened", but just as easily that rainy day could have been a sunny one. A roll of the dice, so the mind must learn to not over-attach to the random and mistake it as 'authentic'. That tricky word again! It is not "more real" that someone somewhere in your history may have said something foolish to you, or made you feel less than you are, at an important stage of your development. Stop giving them a power over you that is not theirs to have. You can gain the wisdom to correct that moment with a better outcome through replay. This is *your* script. Retake your power and give yourself the support of positive affirmation, with the reinforcement of corrective visualization. This is a similar exercise to Freud's theory of healing trauma by making the unconscious conscious, then re-experiencing the negative event. Where through this catharsis, you safely correct it. But here, we apply more active, intentional remedy.

I think of a wildlife series on TV, where a lion alone was surrounded by twenty hyenas and the worry in his face as they bit to his right and left hindquarters. And how that worried face changed when his friend, another male lion, came rushing over from out of nowhere and scattered the hyenas. 20 hyenas against one lion classifies as kitty trouble, but two lions are plenty to dispatch an entire gang of irritating howling thugs with horrid breath and terrible cackle. After the easy dismantling of their hideous foes, the lions rolled in the grass rubbing their manes and cheeks together, being so thankful. Take that feeling of gratefulness from any time when you were saved from what seemed a catastrophic situation, and send that joyful emotion into all your cells, so you too can be saved today by that lion.

Using the priceless gift of reimagining does not deny what has been difficult but is learning to say yes to our trials, by returning to them with reinforcements. Then we let the light IN to these moments and watch them grow into possibly something even approaching beautiful, as our perspective evolves to see purpose in adversity. And because it is a generous universe, based on its ripping apart of forms into new dynamic energetic currents, there is always another opportunity to try again, in some time, in some vast world.

The windshield wipers on my goggles sweep and clean, removing residue of unwanted influence. The subtle hues of the makeup mirror surround the vessel, searching for any hidden poisons that must be further extracted.

I spoke with a client last week whose father had not believed in his talent growing up, who wanted him to take the path of a banker. The secure path. I asked him to visualize his father's love in how it sought to protect him, rather than the form he perceived; the rejection he felt in not being recognized for his special gifts. Supporting, he thought, the wrong thing. So now we reshape the message of disbelief in him that he had incorrectly internalized, by converting the protective support that was originally intended, into the very belief his son had wished for. Experience what it feels like to have that approval now, and inject that goodness also into your life experience. Re-teach your neurons a new cellular configuration.

I will be the first to admit that there are certainly some professionals in the field of psychology who might say this is a form of denial, to override the experiences "you did have" with elements of dreaming, of the imaginative. This firstly ignores the degree to which we do dream our realities into being. But more importantly, on an early-development planet like Earth, the truth is that many experts in any field are frankly beginners in the realms of consciousness and activation, and are as beguiled by the tricks of maya as their soul's grade-level permits them. Like the cat that can only reach the level that is cat. When you can see past the construction of reality, the veil, and are no longer trapped in the mundane dictates of a fixed coordinate world, you will discover the flexibility of the gears. That your imagination and the power to visualize is more than just an artist's tool. We can unravel perceived occurrence and yes, in doing so, we CAN rewrite our script.

We must learn from the lion of swiftly rising to readiness for momentary battles, but also learn from the unicorns, who protect themselves by remaining unguarded. We must never be so fooled by the dramas of external reality as to become one of the joyless. For then, we become fools indeed.

As my zero-gravity chair evenly distributes the weight of my physical form in a tension-disbursing experience of floatation, and the tiny salt particles open my lungs, calming my nervous system as it penetrates my skin, and which —in concert with neurotransmitters— allow the mind its full wing expansion, I feel in this moment ageless; an unadulterated immediacy that is the audacity of youth.

This is after all why the Ancient Egyptians embalmed King Tut with a full erection, to challenge even the gods with the mighty virility of the child king's remarkable 19-year-old phallus, on fully engorged display.

Also of pertinent interest, there was a hidden dagger placed in the wrappings around the pharaoh's right thigh, with an iron blade intersected by a golden handle, topped with a round crystal knob. Iron was considered more valuable than gold at that time because it was such a rare mineral then, and archeologists believe, as tests on the material seem to also suggest, the iron came directly from a meteor that had fallen from outer space. This child king was truly David Bowie over three millennia before rock music was born.

And jet setting across this span of time brings us to perhaps the most important point considering the dynamics of youth and aging: what even is the past and future in a multiverse such as ours? The great thing about the Cellular Game of our Holographic Universe —that every cell exists within every other— is that if you were alive for just one second, you're alive forever.

If you ever feel the weight of the world crashing down upon you, take a moment to recall you are on One of Billions of Developing Planets, at just one fleeting moment. Escape your ingrained myopia! Hold the view of seeing yourself from space, just a dot in the cosmos of time, a grain of sand in the wind. Then whatever awful thing may disturb you and send you into a spiral, further ask how many magnificent glorious things are happening —all over— that you are not aware of? From the feline purr of a spotted leopard, to a new play written, to a bright new engagement of a daring voyage... or somewhere, a saying of "Yes" against whatever great darkness is meant to dampen it.

I lean into my helmet's mouthpiece and proclaim:

"Keep

Your

Imagination."

A bell rings from outside the door. The session is up. The lights around the DNA Psyche Converter fade until the form of the vehicle has dissipated into micro-particles of salt. My wonderful fantasy outfit replaced by my wonderful reality outfit. A sense of time rooted in the stars and astral destiny.

Walking out to greet Esmerelda, the sky opens up to rain, with no facsimile of droplets. All the real thing. The engine thunders back in a way only older engines do, and the radio connects to signal.

  RADIO REPORT: — "MAGIC IN THE AIR" BY BADLY DRAWN BOY— IS PLAYING.

SEQUENCE EIGHTEEN

Zozobra is a unique annual event in Santa Fe, kicking off a week-long celebration known as Fiestas, honoring the reclamation of the city under Spanish rule. While Fiestas dates all the way back to the early 1700s, Zozobra started in the 1920s, an invention of Will Shuster, another Anglo artist from the East Coast, like Meem, that has deeply penetrated the Santa Fe experience and which has been transmuted into local tradition. With roots long before Burning Man, this is a 50-foot-tall marionette that is burned as part of, essentially, a citywide public pagan ceremony. For the kids who grow up here, it's a combination of Halloween and the 4th of July, with an element of local personal mythology thrown in, that sets it apart from anything experienced anywhere else. This yearly burn held on the final Friday of Labor Day weekend, attracts 60,000 people from near and far, close to matching the city's entire population, all gathered in Fort Marcy Park, to end the summer with a definitive and eye-popping bang.

The real witchcraft is how locals provide the material for what is burned inside the giant doll. Love letters, parking tickets, old taxes, college rejections, bad news medical records, pictures, or just a written scrawl of what a resident would like to set aflame, to be cleansed before entering into the new year, just in advance of the autumnal equinox. To release all of the City's gloom being carried, and ritualistically have it sent forth into the fire. How real is such a ceremony? That depends on how much you tune into what is unfolding, and how seriously you take the inner journey to liberate the past, amid the fireworks pounding the sky overhead and kids flapping Zozobra dolls in the air.

As the huge puppet, with arms waving, screams its dread, a visual story seems to unfold, with dynamic pyrotechnics accentuating the hulking creature's struggle against the yelling of the crowd. Most of us, if surrounded by a bunch of rowdy Southerners, collectively screaming "B U R N H I M!" would definitely head for the hills to take cover. But it's a powerful symbolic release— except for the fact that he really does burn to the ground in a gargantuan explosion of ash and awe.

I see a happy sight from across the field, as Gunner comes running over. His dashing smile bellies playful intent as he hands me a Zozobra doll. I laugh. "Look at you, cowboy!" He kisses my cheek, and says, "You really get around, been watching you on Instagram you know." "Where you've been rather silent," I reply. "Feel camera shy?"

"Let's just say I'm attending Zozo this year for a purpose," he says, "I've got some things to let go of." That gave me a hint of alarm, but he quickly follows with, "I put my portion of the manuscript in the big guy!" and points to Zozobra.

"That one message you sent me on Instagram in response to my post 'Give me one sentence that sums up fame', do you remember what you said?"

I make a face to remember. "You wrote, 'There is no less sturdy a platform on which to stand than other people's approval' and it really hit home to me, that it was glorifying the popularity contest of celebrity and equating that with success... when I rarely agree with what popular opinion thinks, myself. Why would I magnify that?"

I teasingly put both hands across my cheeks in play amazement. I am of course pleased by his processing the deeply embedded false messaging of our image-obsessed world, but the issue is even bigger than that. There are only two possibilities: either it is true that only a tiny handful of celebrated people represent the lives that have mattered in this world, or all of the struggles, insights, late night conversations, early morning gatherings, and each hug and kiss and slap all across the world is the human history that represents our collective legacy. I am on the side of those many billions of people as to whose stories matter in that equation. You can't believe in humanity and have it any other way.

But I just reply, "My work here is done," and tap his arm. "I decided I wanted to work for Nobody Magazine," he says. "Awww," I say, with a sweet gleam in my eyes and a soft recognition in the heart.

He smiles again but the light facade of levity falls off, and I see a slight tremble encroach his body. "Gunner?" I reach for his hand. Tears start to form at the corners of his eyes and his mouth clenches shut in sadness even as he tries to form a sentence. After he speaks and shares his gloom, I put my arms around him.

There is nothing more at odds with mood and place than to have intimate conversations in wildly public settings, with party music pumping out of speakers in preparation for an extravagantly explosive event, as an embattled backdrop to the quiet murmurs of personal despair articulated between two people, requiring you to lean close to each other's ears just to hear. But it turns out Gunner has been dealing with the severity of his mother's health. She had experienced early onset dementia and is entering more serious stages. The family has been deciding what steps to take and are already approaching the need to place her in hospice care at only 70 years young. As traumatic as this kind of situation is for any family, watching the people they have known and loved fade into a form of obscurity from their own conscious persona, the horror of the person experiencing it is always foremost in my mind. When I speak of the primitivism of this world's level of culture after centuries of opportunities for advancement, this stands near the top as a clarion example.

Gunner holds out just a paper clip. "I brought the assisted living contract to the gloom bin too," he says.

There is no one who would argue that the most 'humane' thing you can do for a pet when they have reached a certain stage of decline, is to release them from this world. To allow them to leave that pain and anguish behind. Yet the only animal we DON'T extend that compassion to is the human being.

I am particularly proud of New Mexico for being one of just two handfuls of states that does have a 'Death with Dignity' or a Right-to-Die law, for those with terminal illness, in such an instance that a physician can conclusively affirm the patient has only 6 months to live. But you cannot opt for that self-administered medication to bring about a peaceful passing in an instance like dementia, where you could still live four to eight years, or even twenty!

What a horrendous omission from a law meant to exude compassion. Forcibly keeping people alive, who have every right to make a mature rational decision to honorably vacate their bodies, should be listed as a Human Rights Violation by the United Nations. Only then will we truly approach being a humane and advanced civilization.

All our lives, we can pick what type of employment to pursue, pick the people we build our life around or not, choose what city to live in or not, what house to buy. In short, we choose what to do with the fabric of all our days. At least that is the American ideal. And I believe when you have paid your dues to this world, you should legally be given the authority of choice as to whether you wish to remain, based on a number of variables.

The same way you would for your cat, your dog, or anyone frankly that you had any love and respect at all for. While you have such basic rights in Santa Fe, very few countries in the world are as evolved in the conversation, still hiding in caves from the central philosophical questions of life and death, and away from a respect for personal agency in self-determination.

"There was a moment when she wanted to go to Geneva, where they would allow her to take an assessment that showed she was clear-headed in her request, and allow a medically assisted passing," he says. "She didn't want to potentially empty her and our bank accounts in order to keep oxygen in her lungs while living in a condition like, well frankly, like it's become. Where you pee yourself because you can't remember, not WHERE a toilet is, but WHAT a toilet is."

"Oh Gunner I'm so sorry," I tell him. "The indignity is unbearable. It's barbaric."

"She would never choose to live this way," he says, "and yet there is nothing we can do about it."

The truth is, there are just a few confusions standing in the way of basic human decency in this matter, which should be easy enough to clear up. If ever the separation of church and state applied to the laws of human existence, it would be to protect any of us from someone else's fear of the unknown, and whatever imagined rule they hold that their lives are the property of whichever lord. Fine for them! But for those of us who know with great certainty about the abundant states of consciousness that materialize beyond this carnal realm, this backwards ideology is unintelligible and, all tact aside, a primitive refusal to evolve.

Once again, my cat Babette provides an example of a higher comprehension level. When it was time to put her down so that she would be protected from unwarranted degrees of pain and a disintegration of her quality of life, I had laid my head against hers so I could, as I told the vet, "walk her over to the other side, myself." She purred with easy grace as I kissed her forehead and we leaned into one another. Usually the sedation is over within moments. But she just kept purring, as minutes went by. Sensing she was somehow defying the very laws of science to stay with me, I said to her softly in my mind, "It's okay, you can let go now," and I heard the purr go out and return in a whir, as the volume ebbs and flows when you circle a radio away from your ear and back again, out to the perimeter of a circular flow of energy and then return again, three times, each time getting fainter until it trailed away.

When I looked up through my tears, the vet seemed emotional. She said, "I have to tell you something. I've been doing this almost twenty years, but never have I encountered what just happened. She was still purring even after her heart had stopped beating." It had been Babette's final gift to me to communicate from the other side that she was still there, even after her physical form had ceased breathing. Like she was saying, "I'm over here and I'm okay! I made it!" and for me to say back in thought, "I know, little girl."

The choice of Self-Directed-Leaving is not only an issue of dignity but an issue of free will. And I think even with the most minimal effort of thought, everyone knows it. But as with casting the Blank Rune in divinatory practice, the unknowable represented by the Norse god Odin's influence, that of hidden matters, there is an accepted wisdom to trust in the void. But humanity still trusts in fear. Ironically, feeling somehow a misguided instinct, that fear is the safe place to cling to.

The mayor is called up to the stage over the loudspeaker. The festivity of Old Man Gloom's death is upon us, for the burning of Zozobra.

Gunner has come here with a few friends, and I clasp his hand as they start moving further into the crowd, bidding him farewell. I send warm light to him in my mind, watching him weave away through the seemingly endless crowd that attends these ceremonies.

As people politely applaud a listing of the sponsors, and the Kiwanis Club that hosts this event essentially to give money back to children's causes in the community, it is once again an incompatible backdrop to the conversation in my thoughts. My mind stays on the inhumanity we are capable of showing each other when held back by fear and ignorance, the continuation of the dark ages from which we have not yet entirely emerged in this world.

There is such a long precedent. Even the infractions of racism are fairly minor if you consider that over the last 300,000 years, there were nine different species of human on this planet, but now only one remains. While existing at different times and with only some overlap, it could still be assumed based on our ruthless competitive spirit in acquiring land and resources that the Homo Sapiens were the last tribe standing by way, most theories suggest, of genocide. Making the way clear from fellow entities also competing at the top-of-the-food-chain, that would have taken resources that we preferred to go to our offspring. In fact, it may have been the first family values campaign.

Not that there have ever been any simple answers. And, of course, we are forged from our struggles. The tennis champion becomes so because she kept striking the balls being fed to her, even when she needed two hands to have the strength to hold the racquet up. She kept hitting until she mastered the art of completing the stroke with follow through, kept stepping forward toward the action and not waiting for the ball to come to her, then kept developing early preparation, to move her feet more, to concentrate more, living in the moment more. So that she can become a killer and lift a trophy.

A young girl holding sticks of fire dances in flowing motions, teasing with her gestures towards the massive beast, hinting at the intention to burn him down. The crowd grows restless after so much waiting. She dances back down the long staircase to the rhythmic chanting of tribal drumming and sound effects that fill the air. Then once again she leads in graceful steps back up the stairs.

Just as in ancient times, there is a sense of how staircases lead up to places of worship, the steps we take by foot, elevating us to speak with gods. Zozobra is no god, Zozobra is an idea. Not just of glooms we carry, but of fears we carry. Our fear of the dark from not knowing what lay out there, or more often perhaps, that which lays within.

RELEASE THIS INTO THE AIR AROUND YOU!

A line of dancers enters, as the orchestra at the bottom of the outdoor stage builds a rhythm of intensity. Each dancer has a torch. Each dancer has an emotion and a willpower, fighting past fear to rid their spirit of what ails them. To rid their memory of an experience they want transmuted. These dancers join in their power, fire jugglers and winged fire birds!

I think of my conversation with Gunner at Andiamo, suddenly recalling that he was moved to get involved with the interview book because of his mother buying celebrity magazines at the grocery. You just never know what people are really going through, what is ticking in them. He was doing this as a way to keep a connection with his mother, while she had been losing her ability to connect with him in their lives, as she was fading from the ability to converse. He was honoring her. But he moved past that interim substitution for connection to her, to honor her better, by honoring the evolution of his own knowing.

The first firework explodes behind Zozobra, and a tear drips down my right cheek.

I think about how many substitutions are standing in as placeholders for people's deeper sublimated selves, as I look at row after row of the tops of beautiful heads, going in all directions in front, to the sides, and in back of me. In reconciling our identity and our happiness to whatever circumstances surround us, could so many illusions be identified and burned with Zozobra tonight and vanquished.

RELEASE THIS INTO THE AIR AROUND YOU!

There is a level at which we incarnate into experiences to evolve past whatever cage ensnares us, to learn its ways, and unwrap the dressings placed upon us, and stand naked and glorious before our own revealing light. Take off those adornments that dress up someone else's dream of you, someone else's hopes affixed to your star, and honor only that which makes you resonate and radiate. Build a new kingdom in you.

RELEASE THIS INTO THE AIR AROUND YOU!

Fireworks scatter above the mammoth marionette, whose head turns to the right and left, eyes lit up by green beams of light, and a throaty scream of protest emanates from its open mouth. The crowd's chants of 'Burn Him' increase. The dancer gets closer to her target.

I close my eyes and listen to the vibrations that fill Fort Marcy Park. I feel symbols of Ancient Egypt, the land of god kings, where only the most complete angles were represented in drawings, presenting face and limbs in profile, yet the eyes always shown facing frontally. Complete and whole. With green malachite and kohl for eye makeup, ointments and perfumes in calcite jars, striking jewelry, all of these applied and worn by both the men and women alike.

In my mind's eye, I see the shepherd's crook and flail in motion, the pyramid composed of so many steps, and feel the wings of the eagle, sacred bird of the city of the sun, expand powerfully from my chest. I open my eyes and witness explosions cascade across the long strings leading to the arms of the creature lumbering above the city, who growls his opposition.

There are moments with the gentle lights sparkling across the sky, where the artful display framing this towering embodiment is so poetic for an instant, Zozo appears like a monster version of Edith Piaf. But with such a more terrible and ragged voice. And you know the fateful blow has been made, as the dancers have fled and a red light appears in the beast's mouth. Fire has come.

RELEASE THIS INTO THE AIR AROUND YOU!

How do we employ the shepherd's staff to pull away those illusions that bind and build for ourselves a path to personal freedom. While we are all enslaved by some level of demands put upon us that we must answer to, the gift we receive in return is to exist in concert with everything else. While freedom can mean getting away from everything, it can also be found in being of service to others. It can be found in private dreaming, free of entanglement, or within the confines of relationship. Whether climbing the ranks of accomplishment for greater financial access, or instead finding validation in uncovering the universe's mysteries and giving them form in new sometimes intangible expression, our professions and pocketbooks don't determine how liberated we become. Freedom is found in jagged lines, inches at a time in different directions. Some fear such amorphous territories but the formless is in union with the gravitational pull of the planet's emotions, the water, which is risen in conversation with the moon, symbol of the feminine and the hidden unknowable, the beauty of walking unseen in the world. This is what Santa Fe is all about after all. The sweet, small, secret glitterings that energetically gather off the beaten path.

The jet fuel of our freedom is unleashed in discovering how to live our dreams. But what even are they? There's this broken idea that dreams must be grandiose things. But like our friend the jumping spider, they can be tiny and complex. The simple desire to be a dancer, an ice skater, a choreographer. To open an ice cream shop. To develop a strain of grapes and start a winery. Or to come up with services and ways forward that no one knew they needed, but which changes the way the world does some aspect of living. Or to find a path beyond working.

Someone's dream could be simply to make people happy, without any specific form in mind whatsoever.

But in all cases, it is about the light we put out into the world.

And fate steps in all the time in people's lives, from plumbers, to bankers, to skateboarders, to singers, just every kind of ordinary person on ordinary paths— in each case to connect us to our dreams and destinies. To materialize that star hidden like a seed within us. And you can become a star in a much more real way than your childhood mind could ever comprehend. Because becoming a star is an inside job, in how you connect to the universe and expand your consciousness toward the corners of the cosmos, like fireworks exploding far above you and out into the inexhaustible.

It is even possible to far surpass all the limits of what you believed your life could ever be, and pave a path that transcends your destiny.

As the fire finally starts to tear through Zozobra, his yells increase. All resistance is released, and an entire City collectively sheds disappointment and darkness to prepare for new emergence. Zozobra's arm separates from his body and crashes to the ground. It's curtains for Big Z.

There is so much weed in the air. Flying high, assured... I head back through the crowd toward the car. I walk so fast making a path past all the strutting shoes and giggling voices, that it seems almost to happen in slow motion.

I unlock the door to Esmerelda and get in, placing the Zozobra doll in the passenger seat. Starting the engine, I look up the road, and the traffic getting home after such a huge event is bumper to bumper. It's the only occasion of the year when a city this small really experiences a true traffic jam. The red lights from people's brakes in front of me, flash across my face.

Thinking quickly, I turn the car around, and head down a little-utilized side street. It's then that the road seems to take on the feel of a tunnel. There is a sense of wind gathering around the car, and an edge of light around the perimeter of the side panels. Before I can identify what's happening, Esmerelda lifts as if by magic into the air... I press the gas and then the break and then the gas again, but I am not in control now. There are forces greater than our attempts to control, to steer. I roll down the windows, not in panic— but in order to catch a better view. The car whizzes above the tree line, and above the streetlights. The motions of life seen from above appear so much smaller and contained than they do at ground level, everything in miniature. But the sky, the sky seems infinite.

Rising like a vision of Santa's sleigh against the backdrop of the moon, I get a quick view of the patio at Palace Prime below, and catch a blurred glimpse of some people enjoying a drink in the warm night air. I put my hands over my eyes as one almost trips, spying Esmeralda in the sky just as he looks up at his glass, making a toast.

Then shimmering above the intersection where North Guadalupe becomes South Guadalupe, it's only a few moments before I see revelers in the Railyard, who start to become just dots of different colors stirring. And with nothing material restraining me, I slip out of even this flying chariot, like a rainbow wave of liquid. But I am still floating in air bubbles, buoyed by an anti-gravitational pull, above even Esmerelda.

And the sky opens up.

And the sky opens up.

And the sky opens up.

Lights, it seems, a mile wide across the expanse above me, blinking and calling, in a hushed peace, a color spectrum that mixes vibes of tranquility and innovation. A circular doorway opens from the center of those lights, and a beam like a stairway to the pantheon of the gods appears.

I have no fear.

The radio which had been off, pops on, its light shining in the dashboard, as the car wheels spin of their own accord.

RADIO REPORT — "LET THE GOOD TIMES BEGIN" BY THE GENTLE WAVES— PLAYS.

And up go I.

And up go I.

And up go I.

I keep my pinky outstretched.

AUTO ANTENNA
Soundtrack Album

 FULL RADIO REPORT:
   Jewels & Fur by Galactic Witchcraft
   Pretty Baby by Blondie
   Strange Powers by The Magnetic Fields
   Can't Stop The World by The Go-Go's
Concerning the UFO Sighting by Sufjan Stevens
Come A Little Bit Closer by Fleetwood Mac
Modern TV by The Cleaners From Venus
33 "GOD" by Bon Iver
She Bop by Cyndi Lauper
Fall In Love With Me by Iggy Pop
Afraid by Nico
Mystic by Galactic Witchcraft
I Want To See The Bright Lights Tonight by Richard and Linda Thompson
A Thousand Suns by Casker
Holy Ghost by Travis Bretzer
Loving Is Easy by Rex Orange County with Benny Sings
You're My Favorite Waste Of Time by Marshall Crenshaw
Magic In The Air by Badly Drawn Boy
Video Life by Chris Spedding
Outer Space by John Grant
Mirrors by Galactic Witchcraft
Only You by Yaz
Let The Good Times Begin by The Gentle Waves

Made in United States
North Haven, CT
22 March 2025

67062583R00114